The Environmental Impact Handbook

Robert W. Burchell
David Listokin

In collaboration with:
RICHARD E. BRAIL, VIVIAN N. BROWN, JOHN BURRITT,
STEVEN I. GORDON, MICHAEL R. GREENBERG, DAVID T. GREIS,
GEORGE HAGEVIK, MICHAEL STRANGE

CENTER FOR URBAN POLICY RESEARCH
RUTGERS—THE STATE UNIVERSITY
NEW BRUNSWICK, NEW JERSEY

About the authors:

Robert W. Burchell is an associate research professor at the Center for Urban Policy Research, Rutgers University.
David Listokin is a research associate at the Center.

About the Center:

The Center for Urban Policy Research, a part of Rutgers, the State University of New Jersey, promotes multidisciplinary investigation into virtually every aspect of urban and suburban life. As its title implies, the Center is concerned with both the academic quality of urban research and the practical application of research results to policy problems. Under the directorship of George Sternlieb, a staff of economists, geographers, sociologists, and urban planners conducts research on housing problems, economic development, organizational dynamics, and other topics at the federal, state, and municipal level.

Studies are now underway at the Center on municipal tax delinquency, neighborhood decline and preservation, housing finance, rent control, condominium conversion, computer mapping, and cost-revenue analysis. Final reports on these subjects will be forthcoming soon.

The Center's publications are available by writing to:

The Center for Urban Policy Research
Rutgers University
Building 4051—Kilmer Campus
New Brunswick, New Jersey 08903

CONTENTS

The federal government is approaching its fifth year of experience with the use of environmental impact statements (EIS). The requirement of an EIS for a major federal action significantly affecting the human environment began with the passage of the National Environmental Policy Act (NEPA) of 1969. Section 102 (2) (C) of the act sets forth the EIS requirement. The significance of this requirement was not initially apparent to most government agencies or to private industry; however, subsequent litigation has shown that the EIS concept has very important implications for the planning and regulation of land use.

Initially there were few guidelines as to what the statements should include and consequently there was a great deal of confusion on the part of both the preparers and the reviewers. Even now, despite the issuance of guidelines by the Council on Environmental Quality and other federal agencies, the content and utilization of EIS's continues to be the subject of debate and litigation.

Despite these and other problems, EIS procedures have had the effect of substantially raising the general level of consciousness regarding the environmental effects of development and the concept has been widely accepted by public policy-makers and environmentalists as a technique for managing growth. Unfortunately, the technique is often misused or underused. On the one hand, growth opponents delight in the delays inherent in the EIS review process and use the requirement to effectively block development. On the other hand, many developers have undertaken extraordinary efforts to document potential environmental effects and planned measures to mitigate those effects, only to find that public agencies have neither the capacity nor desire to properly use the information.

Now many states and local governments have taken steps to require environmental impact statements for various types of development. Some of the legislation requires state agencies to file reports, some requires the private sector to comply with filing requirements. The only model legislation in these areas is provided by the National Environmental Policy Act. At best this can only be called an unfortunate situation. Not only are there many problems yet to be ironed out with the federal approach, but there is an even more serious question as to just how the EIS concept should be integrated into the very complex set of existing state and local controls affecting land use. In short, the public policy context in which the EIS is to be used at the state and local level is very different than that at the federal level..How can the EIS process be made compatible with zoning, subdivision regulations, comprehensive planning, and other regulations? What is permissible under zoning may have adverse environmental effects; or what is desirable environmentally may not be a permissible use. How can these and other problems be ironed out in an equitable manner?

Other questions yet to be resolved include:

1. Who should pay the cost of preparing EIS's and conducting the necessary background studies? In particular, what will be the effect on the consumer?

2. Can EIS requirements be standardized? Can the standards considered during the process be made more explicit? Can the timing of the review process be made more predictable?

3. Can localities develop data bases to reduce the need for redundant surveys each time an EIS is required?

4. Can localities afford complex EIS procedures? Will competent personnel be available to prepare or review required submissions? What is the threshold level of government with adequate capacity to manage an EIS program?

5. What scale projects should be subjected to EIS requirements?

This handbook is a partial response to some of these questions. In particular it deals effectively with the matter of standardization. While it would be desirable to have attempted the preparation of a comprehensive handbook with convincing answers to all possible questions that might be asked by state and local officials as well as affected developers, the tide of events does not permit such a luxury. The answers to some questions will require extended research and investigation, and in some cases the answers will only come through experience. In the meantime there is an urgent need in both the public and private sectors for guidance in the development and implementation of EIS policy.

The handbook makes a major contribution to the EIS field by intelligently distilling a vast array of information developed as a result of the federal experience and early state experiences. It presents a standardized approach to EIS procedures and requirements.

It will be very useful to persons attempting to lay a proper foundation for decision-making, giving both the public and private sector a complete listing of the kinds of information required to evaluate the merits of proposals and the merits of potential court challenges. The application of the handbook guidelines to any local situation, however, must be done with great care and discretion. Each state, locality, and project will have particular characteristics which dictate the appropriate level of investigation, type of data required, and extent of review and analysis. The handbook does not define "*the* right approach," only the array of "right approaches" that should be considered on a selective basis by those responsible for undertaking development and establishing local policy.

While the handbook's approach to standardization is useful, its limitations must be recognized by all readers and users of the information. The concepts with which this book deals are embryonic. There will be much to be added in the future as a result of research, experience, and the formulation of legal doctrine.

Nevertheless, movement toward the development of better urban environments is an incremental process. The EIS concept is an important improvement in procedures for arriving at more informed choices among a series of alternatives and it encourages environmentally sound development, a standard the Urban Land Institute has promoted for many years. The handbook provides important information that can lead to improving the EIS process on an incremental basis. This is a matter that must receive serious consideration by all persons, both in public and private capacities, who support the concept of a "decent home and living environment for all American families."

The Urban Land Institute

In 1973, over 2,000 environmental impact statements were prepared at the federal level and submitted to the Council on Environmental Quality. Planners/geographers at Rutgers University have studied the adequacy of the environmental analyses presented in a 10 percent sample of these statements.[1] Their preliminary conclusion is that the majority of the impact statements fail to present sufficient information to allow a neutral decision-maker to judge the importance of the environmental benefits and costs of the proposed projects. Other investigators, for example, the Center for Science in the Public Interest and the Environmental Protection Agency (EPA) have drawn similar conclusions.[2] EPA's negative ratings are especially important because its staff is more environmentally oriented than the other federal agencies charged with reviewing impact statements. Furthermore, the proportion of statements labelled by EPA as presenting insufficient information for making a decision has been increasing—a finding which does not support the standard contention that the quality of the statements will improve with experience.

When diverse academic, private, and government analysts find that more than 40 percent of the impact statements are not sufficiently detailed to provide the basis for a decision, one must conclude that either many consulting firms and agencies are poorly prepared and/or are ignoring the mandate of the National Environmental Policy Act of 1969,[3] or the guidelines that channel their responses are weak and ill defined. At the federal level, rhetoric is aimed at convincing the public that national policies are being brought into line with modern concerns for the quality of life.[4] However, the nuts-and-bolts analyses frequently read more like advertisements rather than objective and comprehensive scientific studies.

If EIS is embraced massively at the local level, a similar track record would be intolerable. It is the purpose of this handbook to mitigate the possibility of such an occurrence by bringing the environmental impact statement into closer line with the espoused objectives of environmental review.

Michael R. Greenberg

NOTES

1. Michael R. Greenberg, John Caruana, and Thomas Peterson, "EPA's Ratings of Environmental Impact Statements: A Test of Regional Characteristics Hypothesized to be Associated with the Ratings," New Brunswick, N.J., Rutgers University, 1974 (unpublished).

2. See J. B. Sullivan and A. S. Farber, "NEPA: Getting Citizens into the Act," *Environmental Action*, September 1973, pp. 13-15.

3. Michael R. Greenberg and Robert W. Hordon, "Environmental Impact Statements: Some Annoying Questions," *Journal of the American Institute of Planners*, May 1974.

4. J. L. Sax, "The Search for Environmental Quality: The Role of the Courts" in H. W. Helfrich, Jr., ed., *The Environmental Crisis*, New Haven, Conn., Yale University Press, 1970, 187 pp.

In a guide reproduced by a state government to provide structure for the massive growth of environmental commissions at the local level, a glossary of terms, not terribly dissimilar from the one included in this document, is enclosed. The glossary defines an environmental impact statement as:

> A document prepared by a *federal* agency on the environmental impact of its proposals for legislation and other major actions significantly affecting the quality of the human environment. Environmental impact statements are used as tools for decision making and are required by the National Environmental Policy Act.[1] (emphasis added)

This definition is indeed dated. EIS is no longer an exclusively federal procedure, for there has been considerable growth at the state, county, and local levels. And except for California and a few other areas, there is not even the polite deference to call something other than the federal environmental impact assessment an environmental "report" rather than a "statement." In the Northeast, Midwest, Southeast, and Southwest, it is EIS rather than EIR because practitioners at the local level have decided through their state enabling legislation and derivative local ordinances that they are in the business and they will dictate the jargon.

The Citizens Advisory Committee points out that urbanization with its concomitant maze of decisions affecting the use, development, maintenance, and redevelopment of land, is perhaps the most important determinant of environmental quality, particularly in the areas where the vast majority of our citizens live. Most of these decisions are made at the local level, influenced by local public investments, regulative ordinances, and economic incentive devices. The effective participation of local urban government is crucial, but now its role is weak, underutilized, and poorly understood.[2]

This handbook recognizes EIS as a local consideration. It takes the procedural aspects of EIS from the realm of the federal bureaucrat and places them at the feet of the local official—exactly where the environmental action is.[3] This approach was not conceived in haste but rather in response to recent legislation also heading in this direction. Section 104(h) of Title I of the Housing and Community Development Act of 1974 (Pub L. 93-383, 42 U.S.C. 5301 et. seg) is but one example:

> The bill would authorize a procedure under which community development applicants with approved applications *would assume for specific projects the review and decision-making responsibilities that would apply to the HUD Secretary were he to undertake such projects as Federal projects.* The procedure would eliminate the necessity for Federal environmental statements at the time of the initial application. At the same time, however, the procedure would assure that NEPA policies and protections of the environment continue undiminished.

> The revised procedure would be applied under regulations of the Secretary issued after consultation with the Council on Environmental Quality. *It would require applicants to certify prior to any commitment of any funds for particular projects (other than funds for general planning or environmental study purposes) that they have in fact met all of their environmental responsibilities in accordance with the Secretary's regulations.* Each such certification would have to be approved by the Secretary who would thereby discharge his responsibilities under NEPA with respect to specific projects covered by the certification. The Secretary would be required to wait at least 15 days after receipt before acting upon such a certification, thus giving those who may wish to challenge a certification an opportunity to take appropriate action. That action might include suit against the certifying officer or applicant, who would be required under the amendment to accept the jurisdiction of the Federal courts for purposes of enforcing NEPA, or a request that the Secretary reject the certification. This 15 day period would be in addition to the normal time allowed for review and comment on final impact statements under NEPA procedures.[4] (emphasis added)

The handbook which follows is a "cookbook" of EIS, particularly directed to the housing sector. The handbook thus provides not only recipes for successful meals (logical and comprehensive formats for EIS's), but also sections on who should prepare the meal (who bears EIS responsibility), intranational cooking (EIS procedures throughout the states), how to use the cookbook (handbook employment), the cooking process (EIS review and procedure), and finally, cooking resources (EIS bibliography and available guidelines), and a glossary of cooking terms (EIS terminology).

Quite obviously in preparing a general cookbook there may be several areas which will not tickle the fancy of the EIS gourmet. This indeed is a sacrifice only partly justified by general rather than specific competence. In the area of water supply and water quality we have attempted to provide a more intellectually stimulating approach; however, even this will fall far short for those who have considerable competence in evaluating impacts in specific areas.

This effort has attempted to be comprehensive and technically accurate, but, we hope, not at the expense of being relevant or comprehensible. We have brought together a multidisciplinary team to cover the substantive, procedural, and legal aspects of EIS filings. While their influence is an obvious contribution to each section, it is necessary at the outset to specify their participation:

Dr. George Hagevik and Ms. Vivian N. Brown, Association of Bay Area Governments, San Francisco, California.

The sections on the EIS review process and EIS interpretation. Dr. Hagevik also contributed to the section on methods of air pollution analysis.

Professor Michael R. Greenberg, Department of Urban Studies, Rutgers University, and Professor Robert B. Hordon, Department of Geography, Rutgers University.

The section on methods for water supply, water quality, topography, natural hazards, and solid waste analysis. Professor Greenberg also contributed the section on more quantitative approaches, Appendix C.

Professor Steven I. Gordon, Department of Urban Studies, Rutgers University.

Entire review and restructuring of all sections on methods, particularly extensive procedural additions in the area of topography and soils.

Professor David T. Greis, University of Missouri, Kansas City, School of Law.

The section on legal interpretation of EIS and the legal bibliography, Appendix B.

Professor Richard E. Brail, Department of Urban Planning, Rutgers University, and Dr. Timothy Smith, United States Geological Survey, Reston, Virginia.

Methods of air pollution analysis.

Professor Michael Strange, Department of Civil Engineering, Stockton State College, Galloway Twp., New Jersey.

Portions of solid waste methods analysis.

Mr. John Burritt, Department of Urban Planning, Rutgers University.

Portions of the EIS bibliography and EIS progeny.

The principal authors have prepared all other substantive sections and made decisions on emphasis and format as well as the assembling of the EIS team. While contributing authors have indeed played a large part, the principal authors bear full responsibility for any errors, omissions, or incorrect interpretations this handbook contains.

Robert W. Burchell
David Listokin

NOTES

1. Office of Environmental Services, *Handbook for Environmental Commissioners*, Trenton, N.J., Department of Environmental Protection, January 1974, p. 46.

2. Citizens Advisory Committee on Environmental Quality *Annual Report to the President and to the Council on Environmental Quality for the Year Ending May 1972.* Washington, D.C., U.S. Government Printing Office, 1973.

3. Although clearly the major projects, such as oil ports or power plants, have regional and even national impact.

4. U.S. House of Representatives, 93rd Congress, *Housing and Community Development Act of 1974.*

EIS PROGENY AT STATE, COUNTY, AND LOCAL LEVELS

INTRODUCTION

The National Environmental Policy Act of 1969 (NEPA) was intended to bring fundamental reform to all levels of federal environmental decision-making. Primarily, it mandated a change in the *processes* which were involved.[1] A whole new body of environmental data, factors, and inputs had to be considered before a project or improvement was authorized.

NEPA's underlying premise was that substantive policy decisions would be improved and a better balance would emerge between environmental and development objectives if a broad range of environmental parameters and alternatives to the proposed action were examined well before final decisions were made—at a point where a wide range of options was still open and where modifications to proposals could be more readily made and accepted.[2]

In this era of "creative localism" brought about by a return of the revenue distribution function to lower echelons of governments, states, counties, and municipalities have recognized that their direct actions and indirect sanctions, through the granting of permits, licenses, and so forth, can spur growth which may be environmentally harmful. These levels of government, which experience on a day-to-day basis the presence or absence of development are increasingly aware that they must incorporate environmental concerns in their decision-making processes.[3]

The object of this section is to describe the spread of EIS requirements to lower levels of government. Which jurisdictions at the state, county, and local levels impose EIS requirements? Do state acts resemble closely the structure and form of NEPA? Do the filing requirements under state, county, and local EIS requirements differ from those under NEPA? What aspects of the federal experience do lower level governments wish to replicate—what do they want to do away with?

EIS GROWTH IN THE STATES
Who Has What?

In an *Environmental Law Reporter* article in 1973 Nicolas C. Yost (Deputy Attorney General in charge of the Environmental unit in the California Attorney General's Office) reported on EIS progeny in the states.[4] He drew upon a study done for the Center for California Public Affairs by T.C. Tryzna entitled *Environmental Impact Requirements in the States*[5] and other summaries reproduced in the Council of Environmental Quality's quarterly publication the *102 Monitor*.[6] A year later, Donald G. Hagman, drawing heavily upon these studies attempted to trace directly to NEPA current areas of conflict in interpreting one or more state statute provisions.

At the time Yost reported, seventeen jurisdictions had followed the federal lead in legislating little NEPA's of *general* application (applying to all areas and all development within definitional bounds) or of *limited* application (only applying to certain types of development or in specified geographical areas) or had administratively promulgated NEPA equivalents.

While there is some question as to the discreteness of Yost's categorizations, Rutgers University has employed a similar type of sorting procedure and resurveyed the fifty states to determine the current status of their environmental legislation. As of January 1, 1975, thirty-two states have acted legislatively or administratively to establish NEPA equivalents within the confines of their political jurisdictions.

As shown in exhibit 2-1, areas that have legislatively adopted NEPA equivalents of general applicability are California, Connecticut, Indiana, Maryland, Massachusetts, Minnesota, Montana, North Carolina, Puerto Rico, South Dakota, Vermont, Virginia, Washington, and Wisconsin.[7] Progenitors of similar legislation of limited applicability are Alabama, Arkansas, Colorado, Delaware, Florida, Hawaii, Mississippi, Nevada, New Hampshire, New Jersey, Pennsylvania, and Rhode Island.[8] Administratively promulgated NEPA equivalents are found in Arizona, Michigan, New Mexico, New York, Texas, and Utah.[9] Potential environmental legislation of a similar nature is receiving at least some attention in Alaska, Georgia, Idaho, Illinois, Iowa, Kentucky, Louisiana, Maine, Missouri, North Dakota, Oregon, South Carolina, Washington, D.C., and West Virginia.[10] There is little or no current activity at the state level in terms of developing general environmental policy guides in Kansas, Nebraska, Oklahoma, and Tennessee.[11]

The EIS Requirement of Little NEPA's

The requirement that environmental effects of decisions be considered through the device of the environmental impact statement is surely the most innovative and far-reaching of NEPA's provisions. In one form or another, all thirty-two jurisdictions that have followed the federal lead make use of an EIS provision in their legislation.

As noted by Yost, Indiana, Maryland, Montana, New Mexico, Puerto Rico, and Washington contain almost the identical five EIS requirements of NEPA.[12] Virginia and Michigan add a requirement for the EIS to contain a section discussing mitigation measures which will be taken by the project's sponsor to lessen environmental impact. South Dakota and California not only contain this "mitigation" element, they additionally insert a requirement to discuss the secondary growth-inducing aspects of the development proposal.[13] Finally, Connecticut and Wisconsin ask for a summary of both the cost and benefits of the proposed project—not environmental costs/benefits however, but rather those of an economic nature.[14] Several other states having EIS provisions abridge slightly the five NEPA content requirements. This is true in Arizona, Massachusetts, Michigan, North Carolina, and Virginia.[15]

Of those states which have little NEPA's of limited applicability, EIS requirements are imposed within defined geographic areas for both public and private activities in: Alabama, Delaware, Hawaii, Mississippi, New Hampshire, New Jersey, Pennsylvania, and Rhode Island.[16] In Nevada the submission requirement pertains more to type of activity rather than location; in Florida it pertains to both location and type of activity.[17]

Finally, of those states which administratively impose EIS, Michigan, Texas, and Utah extend the requirement to publicly permitted private activities; Hawaii and New York do not. Arizona requires EIS's of public and private water-oriented development activities.[18]

The Overseeing Agency

The specific department or agency which oversees EIS at the state level is again quite diverse. In California, it is the Secretary of the Resources Agency; in Delaware, the State Planning Office; in Florida, it is a Game and Fresh Water Fish Commission; in Hawaii, an Office of Environmental Quality Control; in Indiana, an Environmental Management Board; in North Carolina, the Department of Natural and Economic Resources; in Washington, the Office of Planning and Program Development in the Department of Ecology and the Ecological Commission; in Wisconsin, the Department of Natural Resources; finally in Puerto Rico, the Environmental Quality Board.[19] In general if a statute is in existence, an existing agency of government, planning board, or department of natural resources is utilized or an independent commission or board is created to oversee impact assessments; both of these types of administering agencies have the power to grant or deny the development request based on potential environmental impact.[20]

In administratively imposed requirements the administering agency frequently is called upon only in an advisory capacity; the decision on the project rests with the line agency or directly with the Office of the Governor.[21]

Applicability of State Law to Local Governments

In the United States the most pervasive of environmental regulations, land use decisions, have traditionally been the prerogative of local government. Zoning and planning, including the conditional uses of land, zoning variances and amendments, touch citizens more directly than most laws pertaining to the environment. Much of the real impact of a state's EIS requirements must therefore depend upon the question of whether those requirements extend to local government's control of the use of land for private activity.[22]

Only the laws of California, Massachusetts, Puerto Rico, and Washington currently impose environmental impact statement requirements upon local governments (Washington's having the broadest applicability of all). North Carolina permits local governments to require environmental impact statements for "major development projects." Montana allows similar authority to become a part of local subdivision regulations. In Puerto Rico's law, although agencies of government are thought to include local political subdivisions, it is still not absolutely clear and is thus far untested. "Home rule" states would probably include environmental review along EIS guidelines as a matter of "right," while other states, such as New Jersey, require that enabling legislation first be enacted to authorize municipalities to require EIS. The nuances of county and local[23] requirements are covered more fully in the following two sections.

COUNTY IMPOSED EIS REQUIREMENTS

EIS progeny at the county level in most instances parallel EIS progeny among states.[24] The counties that impose an EIS requirement frequently derive their authority from a little NEPA (general or limited application) or an administrative equivalent which exists at the state level. The manner in which the EIS regulations have been implemented varies, however, by county. County environmental controls have been adopted in the form of resolution,[25] amendment to the zoning ordinance,[26] amendment to the subdivision ordinance,[27] or through the incorporation into the county charter of an Environmental Bill of Rights,[28] depending upon the state constitutional requirements.

In those counties where EIS applies to publicly permitted or licensed projects or to private projects partially funded with public monies, supervisory authority is usually vested in either the county planning commission or zoning commission. In those cases where EIS is required for projects initiated or fully funded by the county, the EIS responsibility is borne by the agency undertaking or funding the activity. In both cases the position of environmental coordinator is frequently created to oversee the circulation of the environmental impact statement and to coordinate multi-agency participation in its processing. The former situation is indicative of the California (Marin and Sacramento County) experience; the latter of the initial drafts of some of Virginia and Connecticut counties' EIS controls. The County Board of Supervisors or County Commissioners, depending upon the grant of authority under which the planning/zoning board operates, may be called in or required to grant or deny final project approval.

An EIS filing is usually required upon petition for a rezoning or conditional use, rather than upon development in excess of "x" acres. The impact statement itself, if it is determined to be necessary, is relegated to the county staff, independent consultant, the applicant/developer, or any combination of the foregoing.

LOCAL EIS FILINGS

The number of local municipalities that require formal environmental review has increased significantly with the inception of NEPA and the resultant environmental awareness. In all probability the number will continue to increase as more states adopt specific EIS enabling legislation similar to that of North Carolina and Montana, or as localities continue to construe liberally the powers granted them through state planning and zoning enabling legislation.[29]

Although some municipalities have enacted a separate and distinct environmental ordinance based upon the authority derived from an enabling statute, this has not been the most common vehicle through which EIS has been propagated. To date, the most frequent means used to impose the EIS requirement has been through the established land use control mechanisms of zoning, subdivision control, and site plan review.[30] Within this general framework, the EIS most often appears in the form of an amendment to the local zoning ordinance or an ad hoc requirement of the planning board or zoning board of adjustment.

There is some variation in how the local machinery is set in motion, but not a great deal. Most frequently, it is activated above a threshold—for example, residential development above a certain acreage or number of units or nonresidential development above a certain acreage or square footage. This is true in such varied locations as Cherry Hill, N.J.[31] Brookline, Mass.,[32] Lakewood, Colo.,[33] or Pennfield, N.Y.[34] Occasionally an EIS may also be triggered by a petition for a rezoning or under the requirements of a conditional use.[35]

Those who oversee EIS filings at the local level are frequently the planning or zoning commissions; in this case the EIS accompanies the development application along with other documentation (cost-revenue, market analyses) through a rather standard development approval process. The community becomes aware of the contents of the EIS simultaneously with local board members, usually through scheduled public hearings. An Environmental Commission may have been instituted locally and if so may receive the development application and accompanying EIS prior to the public hearing. The commission would then report its findings at the public gathering. In some cases this function may be undertaken by the building inspector or director of public works.[36]

In general, the local EIS requirement extends without exception to the private sector. Despite the comprehensiveness of the EIS application, many localities have failed to follow this requirement up with an equally comprehensive set of guidelines setting forth the criteria that will be used to make environmental judgments and the information required of those who must file.

A SUMMARY OF EIS PROGENY

Exhibit 2-1 provides an up-to-date summary of environmental impact statement requirements at the state, county, and local levels. The data represent legislation as of January 1975 reported by the designated environmental coordinating agency of the specified state. The information for lower levels of government was provided by the state office and subsequently verified by county and local officials.

NOTES

1. See Burton C. Kross, "Preparation of an Environmental Impact Statement," *University of Colorado Law Review*, Vol. 44, 1972. p. 81.

2. See Frederick R. Anderson, "The National Environmental Policy Act: How Is It Working, How Should It Work?" *Environmental Law Reporter,* January 1974.

3. Bowie, Maryland, Commission for Environmental Quality, "The Role of Environmental Impact Statements in Local Government Decisionmaking," *The Urban Lawyer*, Vol. 6, 1974, p. 96.

4. Nicholas C. Yost, "NEPA's Progeny: State Environmental Policy Acts," *Environmental Law Reporter*, Vol. 3, 1973, pp. 50090-50098.

5. Thaddeus C. Tryzna, "Environmental Impact Requirements in the States," *Center for California Public Affairs*, June 1973, p. 20.

6. Council on Environmental Quality, *102 Monitor*, Vol. 3-3, April 1973, p. 21.

7. Yost, "NEPA's Progeny," p. 50090. See also exhibit 2-1 under Maryland, Minnesota, South Dakota, and Vermont.

8. Ibid., p. 50090. See also exhibit 2-1 under Alabama, Colorado, Florida, Mississippi, New Hampshire, New Jersey, Pennsylvania, and Rhode Island.

9. Ibid., p. 50090. See also exhibit 2-1 under New York and Utah.

10. See exhibit 2-1 under listed states.

11. See exhibit 2-1 under listed states.

12. (i) The environmental impact of the proposed action,
     (ii) Any adverse environmental effects which cannot be avoided should the proposal be implemented,
     (iii) Alternatives to the proposed action,
     (iv) The relationship between local short-term uses of man's environment and the maintenance and enhancement of long-term productivity,
     (v) Any irreversible and irretrievable commitments of resources which would be involved in the

proposed action should be implemented.
Yost, "NEPA's Progeny," p. 50094. See exhibit 2-1.

13. Ibid.

14. Ibid.

15. See exhibit 2-1 under listed states.

16. Yost, "NEPA's Progeny," p. 50094. See exhibit 2-1.

17. Ibid.

18. Ibid.

19. Thomas G. Dickert and Katherine R. Domeny, *Environmental Impact Assessment: Guidelines and Commentary*, Berkeley, California, University Extension, University of California, 1974, pp. 195-200.

20. See exhibit 2-1.

21. Ibid.

22. Yost, "NEPA's Progeny," p. 50093.

23. See also Bowie, Maryland, Council on Environmental Quality, "The Role of Environmental Impact Statements."

24. Yost, "NEPA's Progeny," p. 50093.

25. Sacramento County, California, Transylvania County, North Carolina, see exhibit 2-1.

26. Hawaii County, Hawaii, see exhibit 2-1.

27. Blaine County, Idaho, see exhibit 2-1.

28. Suffolk County, New York, see exhibit 2-1.

29. See exhibit 2-1.

30. See Steve Carter, *et al., Environmental Management and Local Government*, Washington, D.C., Washington Environmental Research Center, 1974, pp. 20-23 and 316-319.

31. See exhibit 2-1 under specific locality.

32. Ibid.

33. Ibid.

34. Ibid.

35. Carter, *Environmental Management.*

36. Ibid.

Exhibit 2-1
State, County & Local Requirements/Proposals for Environmental Impact Statements

State/Other Political Subdivision	EIS Requirements and/or Proposals	Contact
ALABAMA	Act 1274 Alabama Law—Regular Session 1973. This act establishes a Coastal Areas Board which may have power to require EIS for activities carried out in coastal areas. Currently, the Board is delineating the area which is to be included in the Coastal Zone.	Deputy Director Ameraport Offshore Harbor and Terminal Commission Bel Aire Mall II, Suite 119 3100 Cottage Hill Mobile, Alabama 36606 Telephone (205) 476-4044
	Outside Coastal Area no EIS is required by State statute. Limited environmental review is required by both Air and Water Pollution Control Commissions.	
	Proposed "Alabama Environmental Land and Water Management Act," to identify and regulate critical areas, died in House Committee, 1973. This bill will be resubmitted in the 1975 session.	Office of State Planning Alabama Director's Office Room 542 State Office Building Montgomery, Alabama 36104
ALASKA	No formal EIS required for either state or private projects. An internal review process is not mandatory but has received wide compliance. All "major" projects are reviewed for comments and recommendations by the Department of Environmental Conservation.	Dept. of Environmental Conservation Pouch O Juneau, Alaska 99801 Telephone (907) 586-6721
Juneau, Alaska	Juneau requires a detailed review of all conditional use applications. This may include an assessment of environmental effects although it is not mandatory.	Juneau Planning/Zoning Commission 155 S. Seward Street Juneau, Alaska 99801 Telephone (907) 586-3300
ARIZONA	Requirements for Environmental Impact Statements Adopted by the Arizona Game and Fish Commission July 2, 1971, it requires an internal review of its own activities.	Chief of Wildlife Planning & Development Division Arizona Game and Fish Department 2222 W. Greenway

Exhibit 2-1
State, County & Local Requirements/Proposals for Environmental Impact Statements

State/Other Political Subdivision	EIS Requirements and/or Proposals	Contact
ARIZONA (continued)	There is no formal EIS requirement for private activity. Proposed: A bill will be submitted in the 1975 session requiring all state agencies involved in an action that would have a significant effect upon the environment to submit a detailed environmental assessment similar to existing federal requirements.	Phoenix, Arizona 85023 Telephone (602) 942-3000
ARKANSAS	Utility Facilities Environmental Protection Act—Act 164 1973—Requires EIS for all utility plant siting with review and comment by all pertinent agencies. The Public Service Commission acts as the lead agency. There are no local requirements for EIS.	Public Service Commission State Capital Building Little Rock, Arkansas 72201 Telephone (501) 371-2051
CALIFORNIA	California Environmental Quality Act of 1970 (Public Resources Code: Section 21000—21174) as amended in 1972, now requires EIS for state, private, and local activities. It is governed by "Guidelines for implementation of the California Environmental Quality Act" which was adopted February 3, 1973, and amended December 17, 1973. Each of the counties and 400 cities is required to adopt its own implementation procedure to meet the above guidelines.	Secretary California Resource Agency Room 1311 1416 Ninth Street Sacramento, California 95814 Telephone (916) 445-9134
Sacramento County	Sacramento County prepares its own EIS in-house, as authorized by county resolution. It covers private actions. A graduated fee schedule is applied to cover costs.	Environmental Coordinator Sacramento County 827 Seventh Street Sacramento, California 95814

Exhibit 2-1
State, County & Local Requirements/Proposals for Environmental Impact Statements

State/Other Political Subdivision	EIS Requirements and/or Proposals	Contact
Marin County	Marin County requires EIS.	Environmental Coordinator Department of Environmental Coordination Marin County Civic Center San Raphael, California 94903 Telephone (415) 479-1100
COLORADO	Amendment Chapter 106 Colorado Revised Statutes 1963 "House Bill 1041"—Incorporates optional environmental review within a coordinated inter-disciplinary approach to land use decision making. The state will provide technical assistance as well as delegate permit authority to any city utilizing a coordinated land use decision making process.	Director Division of Planning Department of Local Affairs Room 524 1575 Sherman Street Denver, Colorado 80203 Telephone (303) 892-2178
City of Lakewood	Environmental assessment is accomplished through the utilization of the provisions of "House Bill 1041" in conjunction with the "Referral Process"; a coordinated review of all local land use decisions by the appropriate departments.	Environmental Control Officer Environmental Control Division 1580 Yarrow Street Lakewood, Colorado 80215 Telephone (303) 234-8674
CONNECTICUT	Connecticut Environmental Policy Act (Public Act No. 73-562) was approved June 22, 1973; it becomes effective February 1, 1975 and will require EIS for state financed projects. Guidelines are currently being prepared. Power Facilities Siting Council may require EIS for power plants. No existing EIS required for private projects. There is cooperative review on larger projects such	Director of Planning and Research Department of Environmental Protection State Office Building Hartford, Connecticut 06115 Telephone (203) 566-4202 Power Facilities Evaluation Council 165 Capitol Avenue Hartford, Connecticut Telephone (203) 566-5612

Exhibit 2-1
State, County & Local Requirements/Proposals for Environmental Impact Statements

State/Other Political Subdivision	EIS Requirements and/or Proposals	Contact
CONNECTICUT (continued)	as new towns. No proposed legislation regarding regulation of private activities.	
	Areas of air, water, solid waste, pesticides, and radiation are covered by permit requirements.	
Town of Glastonbury	Town Ordinance T-17, Section 1741.6 gives the conservation commission review authority over subdivisions.	Environmental Planning Assistant to Conservation Commission Town of Glastonbury Connecticut Telephone (203) 633-5231
	After initial screening based on soils, water tables, topography, etc., a builder may be required to submit an EIS showing measures proposed to overcome difficulties.	
	Guideline used is a system of overlays developed by state extension service based on: Hill & Thomas, "Use of Natural Resources Data in Land and Water Planning," *Bulletin 733*—Connecticut Agricultural Experiment Station (New Haven 1972).	
	Ordinance (Section 3.25 of Building Zone Regulations) requires review by town planning and zoning commission, conservation commission and town engineer for all activities within 100 feet of a brook or wetland or other environmentally fragile areas. The builder must show it will not cause flooding, pollution, or erosion.	
	Inland Wetlands and Water Course Regulations: Regulations are now in existence and require EIS of various uses affecting wetlands areas.	

Exhibit 2-1
State, County & Local Requirements/Proposals for Environmental Impact Statements

State/Other Political Subdivision	EIS Requirements and/or Proposals	Contact
DELAWARE	Coastal Zone Act, Title 7, Delaware Code, Chapter 70 covers 20 percent of the state's land. It requires EIS for industrial activities. Guidelines are found within the Statute.	Chief Coastal Zone Management Delaware State Planning Office 530 S. duPont Highway Dover, Delaware 19901 Telephone (302) 678-4271
	Wetlands Law, Title 7, Delaware Code, Chapter 66, calls for an EIS before a permit will be issued for fill projects. The permit is issued by State Department of Natural Resources and Environmental Control; mapping is currently underway.	
	Coastal Zone Management Program: The state is participating in a 3-year study of the coastal zone in accordance with federal regulations.	
	Proposed: New Coastal Zone Act to extend coverage to residential and commercial activities.	
	No acts proposed to cover parts of state not included in coastal zone or wetlands.	
	There are no EIS requirements for state government activities.	
	There are no EIS requirements for private activities.	
FLORIDA	Environmental Control Law, Chapters 253 and 403 Florida Statutes—requires environmental review conducted through permit procedure for construction of power plants and dredge and fill operations.	Director of Environmental Protection Section Florida Game and Freshwater Fish Commission Bryant Building Tallahassee, Florida 32304 Telephone (904) 488-6661
	Florida Environmental Land and Water Management Act of 1972, Chapter 380, Florida Statutes requires a similar review to assess the regional impact of above.	

Exhibit 2-1
State, County & Local Requirements/Proposals for Environmental Impact Statements

State/Other Political Subdivision	EIS Requirements and/or Proposals	Contact
FLORIDA (continued)	No local EIS requirements.	
GEORGIA	No formal EIS requirement for state or private activities. No bills are currently pending; several are drafted but not introduced—it will be a minimum of 1 year before they are complete. State agencies, especially the Department of Transportation, undertake EIS. Roughly follow CEQ guidelines. Most major development projects are federally funded. Therefore NEPA requirements pertain.	Office of Planning and Budget 270 Washington Street, S.W. Atlanta, Georgia 30334 Telephone (404) 656-3861
HAWAII	Act 246, Session Laws of Hawaii, Chapter 343 requires EIS for actions involving state or county land or funds, as well as for a limited range of private activities, namely: (a) any activity in Waikiki area. (b) any amendment to state or county general plans (zoning) except new county plans and amendments made by the county. (c) any activity in the conservation district, which constitutes all of Hawaii's beaches and 60% of its total area. (d) any historic site. (e) all shoreline areas and 300 feet to seaward. The bill also provides a limited standing to sue for persons or agencies who provide substantive comment during the review process.	Director Office of Environmental Quality Control Office of Governor 550 Halekauwila Street Room 301 Honolulu, Hawaii 96813 Telephone (808) 548-6915

Exhibit 2-1
State, County & Local Requirements/Proposals for Environmental Impact Statements

State/Other Political Subdivision	EIS Requirements and/or Proposals	Contact
HAWAII (continued)	In addition, the statute creates the Environmental Quality Commission which is responsible for the development of rules and regulations for the administration of the act.	
County of Hawaii	County Ordinance 1002 passed May 1974 requires EIS covering all large projects such as resort or industrial projects.	County Planning Director County of Hawaii 25 Aupuni Street Hilo, Hawaii 96720 Telephone (808) 961-8288
IDAHO	No formal EIS requirements. Senate Bill 1434—State Mandatory Planning and Zoning Enabling Act would allow localities to require EIS. It was defeated in the 1974 session; however, it will be resubmitted in 1975. Senate Bill 1328—would require review and comment by the Division of Budget, Policy Planning and Coordination. This was defeated in 1974 and will be resubmitted in the 1975 session.	Director State Planning and Community Affairs Agency State House Boise, Idaho 83707 Telephone (208) 384-2287
Blaine County	Ordinance Number 71-3 Section 15—Requires EIS as part of the subdivision controls. It covers county activity; private, residential and industrial developers. EIS has been found to be ineffective. Now implementing performance standards screened by a technical review board.	Administrator Blaine County Planning and Zoning Department Box 149 Hailey, Idaho 83333 Telephone (208) 788-4665
City of Pocatello	Under the site review section of the zoning ordinance a modified EIS report is tied to the issuance of a conditional use permit applicable to any structure over three stories or any public building.	City Manager Box 4169 Pocatello, Idaho 83201 Telephone (208) 232-4311

Exhibit 2-1
State, County & Local Requirements/Proposals for Environmental Impact Statements

State/Other Political Subdivision	EIS Requirements and/or Proposals	Contact
ILLINOIS	No formal EIS requirements. Former Governor Richard B. Ogilvie proposed legislation similar to NEPA in 1972, but it failed to pass. No new bills introduced.	Director State Clearing House Bureau of the Budget Capitol Building Springfield, Illinois 62706 Telephone (217) 782-4520
	No localities require EIS.	
	EIS may be required in the future to cover impact of proposed coal gasification plants; however, implementation has not yet been formalized.	
INDIANA	Indiana Law Section 35-5301 established a little NEPA of general application.	Environmental Management Board 1330 W. Michigan Street Indianapolis, Indiana 46206 Telephone (317) 888-8980
	Public Law 98, 1972 Indiana Code 1971, 13-1-10-3 requires EIS for state activities, explicitly excludes private activities. Regulations to implement this law are not yet promulgated.	
	There is no EIS required for private acts.	
	There are no new proposals.	
	No localities require EIS.	
IOWA	No state requirements for EIS.	Environmental Coordinator Office for Planning and Programming 523 East 12th Street Des Moines, Iowa 50319 Telephone (515) 281-3711
	Senate File 1273—filed March 7, 1974 would have required EIS of public and private activities; however the bill was defeated. No local requirements.	

Exhibit 2-1
State, County & Local Requirements/Proposals for Environmental Impact Statements

State/Other Political Subdivision	EIS Requirements and/or Proposals	Contact
KANSAS	There are no laws requiring EIS. No laws are proposed. No localities currently require an EIS.	Director Division of Environment Department of Health & Environment Topeka, Kansas 66620 Telephone (913) 296-3821
KENTUCKY	No EIS requirements. Several land use proposals for critical areas have been introduced in the legislature, but would not require an EIS. No localities have EIS requirements.	Executive Assistant Department of Natural Resources and Environmental Protection 6th Floor Capitol Plaza Tower Frankfort, Kentucky 40601 Telephone (502) 564-7320
LOUISIANA	Scenic Rivers Law—Act 398-1970 requires any project involving any of 38 subject rivers to file an environmental assessment to be reviewed by the Wildlife and Fisheries Commission. Proposed: (House Bill 1150) failed to pass in 1972. No new proposals since. No localities have requirements for EIS.	Director Wildlife and Fisheries Commission P.O. Box 145 26 South East Station Baton Rouge, Louisiana 70808 Telephone (504) 389-6421
MAINE	There are no laws requiring EIS. None are in preparation. No EIS required for State Government. No localities have EIS requirements.	Commissioner Department of Environmental Protection State Street Augusta, Maine 04330 Telephone (207) 289-2811

Exhibit 2-1
State, County & Local Requirements/Proposals for Environmental Impact Statements

State/Other Political Subdivision	EIS Requirements and/or Proposals	Contact
MAINE (continued)	Site Location Law, Title 38, Sections 481-488, Maine Statutes requires environmental review.	
MARYLAND	Maryland Environmental Policy Act (1973) (Sections 447 to 451, Article 41, Annotated Code of Maryland) requires environmental assessment for all requests from State agencies for legislative appropriation or other legislative actions that will alter the quality of the environments.	Clearinghouse Division of State Planning 301 W. Preston Street Baltimore, Maryland 21201 Telephone (301) 383-2467
	No EIS is required for private activities.	Maryland Department of Natural Resources Annapolis, Maryland Telephone (301) 267-5548
Bowie	Bowie Commission for Environmental Quality (BCEQ) was created in May 1971 by an ordinance of the Bowie City Council. The Bowie ordinance "Declaring an Environmental Policy and Providing for Environmental Impact Statements", requires EIS of actions by the City government, and requests for zoning and subdivision decisions.	Vice Chairman 4804 Riverton Lane Bowie, Maryland 20715 Telephone (301) 776-4880
MASSACHUSETTS	Chapter 30, Section 61 and 62, Massachusetts General Laws requires EIS for state activities and for private activities requiring a state license or permit.	Secretary Executive Office of Environmental Affairs 18 Tremont Street Boston, Massachusetts 02408 Telephone (617) 727-7700
	Review governed by: "Regulations to Create Uniform System for the Preparation of Environmental Impact Reports."	
Town of Brookline	Town Ordinance Section 5.09 (Dec. 1971) establishes an "Environmental Impact and Design	Town Clerk's Office 333 Washington Street

Exhibit 2-1
State, County & Local Requirements/Proposals for Environmental Impact Statements

State/Other Political Subdivision	EIS Requirements and/or Proposals	Contact
Town of Brookline (continued)	Review" over five specific street areas and seven types of land use wherever they occur.	P.O. Box 1000 Brookline, Massachusetts 02147
MICHIGAN	Executive Order Number 1974-4—Requires an EIS for both state activities and private activities requiring a permit, when an agency director determines that the action will have a significant effect on the environment. EIS is administered by Michigan Environmental Review Board. A bill is pending to establish a state Environmental Policy Act, patterned after NEPA. There are no local requirements for EIS.	Executive Secretary Environmental Review Board Office of Intergovernmental Relations Department of Management and Budget Lewis Cass Building Lansing, Michigan 48913 Telephone (517) 373-0933
MINNESOTA	Minnesota Environmental Policy Act of 1973 (Minnesota Statutes Annotated Chapter 412 Laws of 1973) requires EIS of both state and private activities. Rules and regulations promulgated April 1974. No localities require EIS.	Director for Environmental Planning State Planning Agency Capitol Square 550 Cedar Street, Room 100 St. Paul, Minnesota 55101 Telephone (612) 296-3985
MISSISSIPPI	Mississippi Coastal Wetlands Protection Act (Chapter 385, Laws of 1973) requires EIS for both private and state activity requiring a permit in coastal wetlands with few exceptions (Port Authority of Biloxi). Outside coastal areas, no EIS is required for state or private acts.	Assistant to the Coordinator Federal-State Program Office of the Governor 510 Lamar Life Building Jackson, Missippi Telephone (601) 354-7570

Exhibit 2-1
State, County & Local Requirements/Proposals for Environmental Impact Statements

State/Other Political Subdivision	EIS Requirements and/or Proposals	Contact
MISSISSIPPI (continued)	None pending. No localities require EIS.	
MISSOURI	No EIS requirements. A bill similar to NEPA is expected for the January 1975 session of Missouri legislature, based on a recently completed report of the Environmental Impact Statement Task Force.	Director State Planning and Analysis P.O. Box 809 Jefferson City, Missouri Telephone (314) 751-3925
MONTANA	Montana Environmental Policy Act, 1971 (Revised Code Montana Section 69-6501 et seq.): Requires EIS for state activities as well as private activities needing permit approval. Covers only activities of executive agencies. Revised guidelines in existence (September 14, 1973).	Executive Director Environmental Quality Council Capitol Station Helena, Montana 59601 Telephone (406) 449-3742
	Strip Mining and Reclamation Law, Strip Mine Siting Act (1974): Requires EIS of both coal mining and power plant construction and activities. Guidelines are available within the acts.	
	Subdivision regulations of 1973 (Revised Code Montana [1974] Section 11-3861 to 3872: Require local governments to perform environmental assessment, with some review powers retained at state level.	
NEBRASKA	No requirements for EIS. None Pending. State Department of Roads does EIS for its own activities.	Comprehensive Planning Coordinator Office of Planning and Programming Box 94601 State Capitol Lincoln, Nebraska 68509 Telephone (402) 471-2414

Exhibit 2-1
State, County & Local Requirements/Proposals for Environmental Impact Statements

State/Other Political Subdivision	EIS Requirements and/or Proposals	Contact
NEBRASKA (continued)	No localities require EIS.	
NEVADA	There are 2 laws requiring EIS: 1. Nevada Clean Air Act, (Nevada Revised Statutes, Chapter 445) as amended in 1971 and 1973 requires an environmental review as part of complex source regulation (effective March 27, 1974). Guidelines are available.	Chief Bureau of Environmental Health Commission of Environmental Protection 1209 Johnson Street Carson City, Nevada 89701 Telephone (702) 885-4670
	2. Utility Environmental Protection Act. Chapter 311, Laws of 1971 (Nevada Revised Statutes, Chapter 704) amended 1973 requires EIS for utility plant siting. To be reviewed by State Environmental Commission. The Environmental Impact Committee makes recommendations to the Environmental Commission which in turn makes recommendations to the Public Service Commission.	Chairman Public Service Commission of Nevada 222 E. Washington Street Carson City, Nevada 89701 Telephone (702) 885-4180
	No further laws are in preparation.	
	No localities require EIS.	
NEW HAMPSHIRE	Sewage Act (New Hampshire Revised Statutes Annotated, Chapter 149E) and Wetlands Act (New Hampshire Revised Statutes Annotated Chapter 431, Sections 1-5) Both exert limited controls. No EIS is required for private or state acts.	Office of Comprehensive Planning Office of the Governor Concord, New Hampshire 03301 Telephone (603) 271-2156

Exhibit 2-1
State, County & Local Requirements/Proposals for Environmental Impact Statements

State/Other Political Subdivision	EIS Requirements and/or Proposals	Contact
NEW HAMPSHIRE (continued)	No bills are proposed.	
	No localities require EIS.	
NEW JERSEY	Wetlands Act of 1970—Requires an EIS for Type B Wetlands permits.	Chief Office of Environmental Review Department of Environmental Protection Trenton, New Jersey 08625 Telephone (609) 292-2662
	Major Coastal Facilities Review Act—Requires an EIS for public acts.	
	Department of Environmental Protection requires, by policy, an EIS for private acts (mostly industrial) requiring multiple permits from DEP.	
	Executive Order Number 53—Requires an EIS on all state funded or sponsored construction projects in excess of $1,000,000 or those less than $1,000,000 but in environmentally sensitive areas. Private acts with state guaranteed loans are also covered.	
	Bonding authorities are not included in above regulations. The Driscoll Expressway Authorization Act requires EIS. Five bills are now pending to require EIS from bonding authorities.	
	The following municipalities require a minimum of environmental review: Bedminster Township Cherry Hill Bernards Township Mine Hill Township Princeton Mendham Boro	
NEW MEXICO	Environmental Quality Control Act, 1971, New	State Planning Officer

Exhibit 2-1
State, County & Local Requirements/Proposals for Environmental Impact Statements

State/Other Political Subdivision	EIS Requirements and/or Proposals	Contact
NEW MEXICO (continued)	Mexico Statutes 12-21-1 et seq.—REPEALED! Subsequent proposals defeated. None are pending. Executive Order Number 72-7 through state clearing house agency oversees approval of each regulatory agency for state funded projects. This may result in environmental assessment; however it is not a formal EIS requirement. There are no local requirements for EIS.	State Planning Office Santa Fe, New Mexico 87501 Telephone (505) 827-5233
NEW YORK	Administrative Regulation (Item 73—Budget Request Manual) requires environmental review and clearance for state activities paid for by ordinary capital funding. (Does not cover state authorities building with bond money.) Guidelines are in the form of a simple check off on pre-printed form (similar to A-95). Rules and regulations in effect (part 615) stipulate that Commissioner of Environmental Conservation may require EIS at his discretion on any permit application before his department. Assembly Bill 11268 was introduced by Joint Legislative Committee on Environmental Conservation which would require EIS on private projects. A similar bill (Assembly 6180-A) covers public acts. Both were defeated in the 1974 Session of the General Assembly.	Director of Environmental Analysis Department of Environmental Conservation Albany, New York 12201 Telephone (518) 457-2223

Exhibit 2-1
State, County & Local Requirements/Proposals for Environmental Impact Statements

State/Other Political Subdivision	EIS Requirements and/or Proposals	Contact
NEW YORK (continued)	Public Service Law—Article 8 requires a Certificate of Environmental Compatibility and Public Needs for the location and siting of major steam electric generating facilities.	
	Strip Mining Bill—mandates an EIS for all new mining operations.	
Suffolk County	The Environmental Bill of Rights provides authority to require EIS on county projects and activities and to establish a Council on Environmental Quality which is mandated to produce guidelines. The "Checklist and Format for Content of Environmental Impact Statements" serves as the working guidelines.	Council on Environmental Quality County of Suffolk H. Lee Dennison Building Veterans Memorial Highway Hauppauge, New York 11787 Telephone (516) 979-2536
Penfield, New York	Town Resolution requires an EIS as part of site plan and plat approval. Review is based on opinions of the various township agencies.	Director of Public Works Penfield Township Penfield, New York 14526 Telephone (716) 377-5500
NORTH CAROLINA	Chapter 1203 (Session Laws of 1971) establishes little NEPA of general application.	Assistant Secretary for Resource Management Department of Natural and Economic Resources P.O. Box 27687 Raleigh, North Carolina 27611 Telephone (919) 829-4984
	North Carolina Environmental Policy Act, 1971 (North Carolina General Statutes, Section 113A et seq.) has been extended to 1977. Requires EIS for state funded project. The act serves as the enabling legislation; however EIS at the local level is strictly optional.	
	Private activities requiring a state permit approval do not need EIS, but entail a minimum of environ-	

Exhibit 2-1
State, County & Local Requirements/Proposals for Environmental Impact Statements

State/Other Political Subdivision	EIS Requirements and/or Proposals	Contact
NORTH CAROLINA (continued)	mental review by the issuing agency. No new laws pending. (Implementation of EIS confined to those agencies with experience through NEPA.)	
Transylvania County	"Transylvania County Environmental Policy Ordinance"—Requires EIS to complement subdivision procedure. It covers earth moving, grading, drainage, road construction and impact on neighboring property.	County Planner Transylvania County Manager's Office 12 E. Main Street Brevard, North Carolina 28712
NORTH DAKOTA	There are no EIS requirements now. Proposal: (not yet submitted as bill) for a "North Dakota Environmental Policy Act of 1975" would require EIS for state activities only. Also proposed "North Dakota Environmental Law Enforcement Act of 1975." It would give citizens standing to sue after meeting certain procedural qualifications. This law would also give the attorney general's office power over all environmental cases. No localities have EIS requirements. The state is facing environmental problems for first time with the growth of coal mining. More environmental regulation is expected.	Director Division of Water Supply and Pollution Control Department of Health State Capitol Bismark, North Dakota 58501 Telephone (701) 224-2386

Exhibit 2-1
State, County & Local Requirements/Proposals for Environmental Impact Statements

State/Local Political Subdivision	EIS Requirements and/or Proposals	Contact
OHIO	There are no state requirements for EIS. None are pending. There are no local requirements for EIS.	Deputy Director for Policy Development Ohio Environmental Protection Agency 450 East Town Street Columbus, Ohio 43216 Telephone (614) 466-8866
OKLAHOMA	There are no state requirements for EIS. None are pending. There are no local requirements for EIS.	Director Oklahoma Department of Pollution Control Box 53504 N.E. 10th and Stonewall Oklahoma City, Oklahoma 73105 Telephone (405) 271-4677
OREGON	There are no state requirements for EIS. A bill to require EIS for state activities (as amended) died in the legislature in the 1973 session. There are no local requirements for EIS.	Assistant to the Governor for Natural Resources 240 Cottage Street Salem, Oregon 97310 Telephone (503) 378-3109
PENNSYLVANIA	Although there are no formal EIS requirements Article 1, Section 27 of the Pennsylvania Constitution establishes a trust for the people of Pennsylvania for the state's natural resources; including clean air, pure water, and the natural, aesthetic, scenic and historic values of the state. The Commonwealth Courts have mandated that the Pennsylvania Department of Transportation and Public	Deputy Secretary for Enforcement General Counsel of Pennsylvania Department of Environmental Review Executive House Office Building 2nd Street Harrisburg, Pennsylvania 17105 Telephone (717) 787-8790

Exhibit 2-1
State, County & Local Requirements/Proposals for Environmental Impact Statements

State/Other Political Subdivision	EIS Requirements and/or Proposals	Contact
PENNSYLVANIA (continued)	Utility Commission consider the environmental effects of their actions.	
	Environmental review is conducted under Solid Waste Management Act, 35 Pennsylvania Statutes, Section 60001 et seq.	
	Clean Streams Act, 35 Pennsylvania Statutes Annotated, 750.1	
	Surface Mining Conservation and Reclamation Act, 52 Pennsylvania Statutes Annotated, 1396.1.	
	Air Pollution Control Act, 35 Pennsylvania Statutes Annotated, 4001.	
	Regulations are promulgated separately for each act by the Environmental Quality Board.	
	There are no local requirements for EIS.	
RHODE ISLAND	Coastal Resource Management Council Act, Fresh Water Wetlands Act, and Inter-Tidal Salt Marsh Act require environmental review.	Statewide Planning Department of Administration 265 Melrose Street Providence, Rhode Island 02907 Telephone (401) 277-2656
	There are no local requirements for EIS.	
SOUTH CAROLINA	There are no state requirements for EIS.	Assistant Director Division of Administration Office of the Governor Edgar A. Brown Building Columbia, South Carolina 29201 Telephone (803) 758-3306
	A proposal for a bill is in the early states of consideration, with no name or number as yet.	
	There are no local requirements for EIS.	
SOUTH DAKOTA	Environmental Policy Act for South Dakota (South Dakota Compiled Laws 11-1A)—Requires	Administrative Services Officer

Exhibit 2-1
State, County & Local Requirements/Proposals for Environmental Impact Statements

State/Other Political Subdivision	EIS Requirements and/or Proposals	Contact
SOUTH DAKOTA (continued)	EIS on all state projects.	Department of Environment Protection State Capitol Pierre, South Dakota 57501 Telephone (605) 224-3351
	There is no coverage for private activity.	
	There are no local requirements for EIS.	
TENNESSEE	There are no state requirements for EIS.	Office of Urban and Federal Affairs 1312 Andrew Jackson Boulevard Nashville, Tennessee 37219 Telephone (615) 741-2714
	None are pending.	
	There are no local requirements for EIS.	
TEXAS	Environment for Tomorrow—The Texas Response— A policy adopted by the Interagency Council on Natural Resources and Environment, effective January 1, 1973, requires EIS for both state and private activities requiring a permit.	Division of Planning Coordination Office of the Governor Box 12428 Capitol Station Austin, Texas 78711
	A bill is being drafted that would make EIS mandatory for state and private activities requiring a permit.	
	There are no local requirements for EIS.	
UTAH	An Executive Order was passed August 27, 1974 for State of Utah and requires EIS for state agencies and an environmental review for private actions receiving permits or licenses.	Environmental Coordinator State Planning Coordinator 118 State Capitol Salt Lake City, Utah 84114 Telephone (801) 328-5245
	There are no local requirements for EIS.	
VERMONT	There are no state requirements for EIS.	Assistant Secretary Agency of Environmental

Exhibit 2-1
State, County & Local Requirements/Proposals for Environmental Impact Statements

State/Other Political Subdivision	EIS Requirements and/or Proposals	Contact
VERMONT (continued)	Act 250 of 1970 (10 Vermont Statutes Annotated, Chapter 151), amended 1973. Any project requiring changes in land use undergoes an environmental review through an administrative hearing process. The act covers both private and state activities. Localities that are affected may participate in state review if they so choose. Procedural administrative regulations are established to accompany this act. There are no local requirements for EIS.	Conservation Montpelier, Vermont 05602 Telephone (802) 828-3309
VIRGINIA	Virginia Chapter 384 approved March 15, 1973 establishes a little NEPA of general application. (Virginia Code Annotated 10-17.107 to 10-17.112) Requires EIS for state activities in the Executive Branch in excess of $100,000 with the exception of highway construction. A "Procedural Manual" is in existence. Statements are filed with the Governor's Council on the Environment. Private activities are not covered by EIS requirements. There are no local EIS requirements.	Environmental Impact Coordinator Council on the Environment Room 1103 8th Street Office Building Richmond, Virginia 23219 Telephone (804) 770-2189
WASHINGTON, D.C.	There are no district requirements for EIS. Currently, at the request of the National	Director Office of Environmental

Exhibit 2-1
State, County & Local Requirements/Proposals for Environmental Impact Statements

State/Other Political Subdivision	EIS Requirements and/or Proposals	Contact
WASHINGTON, D.C. (continued)	Capital Planning Commission a limited environmental assessment is conducted on capital improvements. A proposal for EIS on projects funded by the District of Columbia was shelved temporarily.	Planning Department of Environmental Services 415 Twelfth Street, N.W. Washington, D.C. 20004
	The mayor's office requires EIS for major municipal improvements. EIS is carried out informally, with no written requirements at the suggestion of the courts.	
WASHINGTON	State Environmental Policy Act, 1971 (Chapter 43.21c, Revised Code of Washington) as amended (July 1, 1973) by Substitute Senate Bill 2531 requires EIS and in addition empowered the Department of Ecology to determine EIS requirements for a major action or legislation with a significant effect upon the environment.	Office of Planning and Program Development Department of Ecology Olympia, Washington 98504 Telephone (206) 753-6890
	At local level all cities and counties are required to prepare criteria for implementation of the State Environmental Policy Act.	
	Shoreline Management Act of 1971 is administered to require impact statements to accompany the review of shoreline permits issued which affect any of the 965 subject rivers and streams or 791 subject lakes.	
WEST VIRGINIA	There are no state requirements for EIS.	Director Department of Natural Resources Charleston, West Virginia
	The House passed Bill 741; the Senate delayed a similar bill (Senate Bill 80), which would	

Exhibit 2-1
State, County & Local Requirements/Proposals for Environmental Impact Statements

State/Other Political Subdivision	EIS Requirements and/or Proposals	Contact
WEST VIRGINIA (continued)	have covered state activities. There are no local EIS requirements.	25305 Telephone (304) 348-2754
WISCONSIN	Wisconsin Environmental Policy Act, 1971 (Wisconsin Statute 1.11), Chapter 274, Laws of 1971 and Chapter 273 of the Laws of 1971, require EIS for both private and state activities. It was recently amended to provide consideration of economically disadvantaged persons as effected by environmental controls. There are no localities requiring EIS.	Secretary Department of Natural Resources Box 450 Madison, Wisconsin 53701 Telephone (608) 266-2121
WYOMING	There are no state EIS requirements. Proposed: Utility Siting Bill would require EIS.	Administrative Assistant to the Governor Capitol Building Cheyenne, Wyoming 82001 Telephone (307) 733-4012
Teton County	Teton County Subdivision Ordinance establishes general requirements for EIS which covers private developers. It is currently being amended to make the requirements more specific.	County Attorney Box 1082 Jackson, Wyoming 83014 Telephone (307) 733-5004
PUERTO RICO	Public Environmental Policy Act (Law Number 9, June 18, 1970: 12 Laws of Puerto Rico Annotated Section 1121 et seq.) requires EIS of all government agencies initiating activities or issuing permit. Agencies short of personnel to execute EIS may refer responsibility for first draft to permit applicant. There are no local requirements for EIS.	Executive Director Environmental Quality Board 1550 Ponce de Leon Avenue 4th Floor Santurce, Puerto Rico 00910

OVERVIEW

Environmental impact statements when good can be very good—both helping the developer to build an economically and environmentally sound project and providing planners and local officials with data for making well-informed decisions. When bad, the environmental impact statement can cost time and money, not only during the approval process, but later on in the project's life when unanticipated effects bring grief to consumer, public agency, and, sometimes, developer alike. Nevertheless, despite all the lists, handbooks, guidelines, and manuals available, it is almost as difficult to define a "good" environmental statement as it is to write one.

Practically speaking, adequacy exists in the eyes of the reviewer. Moreover, preparation of a good assessment is no guarantee of speedy processing. Inadequate assessments are often accepted without a murmur, while exhaustive studies may well result in delays if only because they make difficult reading. Before embarking on the preparation of an impact statement, therefore, the developer, public planner, or consultant should be aware not only of the legal requirements, but also the special interests and aspirations of the statement's potential audience. To assist this investigation it is helpful to separate the audience into three groups:

1. Agencies of government which *must* receive the assessment report because they require it as a part of processing or have jurisdiction over some aspect of its approval (for example, the local government or Federal Housing Administration insuring office).

2. Agencies of government which *should* receive the report because they can provide useful information which ought to be known as early as possible. This information may have an effect on future actions related to, if not directly controlling, the project's success (for example,

sanitation districts, school districts, areawide planning organizations, or state agencies).

3. Private and quasi-public organizations and individuals with strong convictions and acknowledged interest in the type of project proposed, the project location, or potential impacts associated with project activities (for example, homeowners associations or conservation and civic groups).

In some cases the local governmental agency will automatically forward completed reports to these agencies and organizations for their review. It is a good idea for the project proponent or report author not only to make sure that this is done, but also to consult these groups while the report is being prepared.

At the outset it should be understood that in all too many cases the environmental impact statement is not used as a means to preserve and enhance the environment, despite the intentions of the myriad statutes and ordinances which require its preparation. Instead, the EIS may be viewed as a tool for the achievement of special interests and aims. These can include gilding a basically ill-conceived project to delude an unsuspecting commission or appealing to the conservationist on residential growth. In these cases even the most comprehensive EIS is likely to be challenged as inadequate. A well-planned and well-researched statement can, however, both anticipate such problems and provide sufficient ammunition to identify their true significance.

Governmental agencies which must receive the report will vary in number and function, depending on the location and nature of the particular project. Thirty-one states and Puerto Rico now require the preparation of some type of impact assessment. Of these, a few, including California, Massachusetts, and Washington, specifically require public agencies to have environmental reports prepared for projects which require a permit, license, or other type of approval. But even in those states where statutes requiring local action have not been enacted, numerous townships, cities, and counties have taken it upon themselves to require submission of an environmental assessment for certain types of projects. Moreover, both the Council of State Governments and the Federal Council on Environmental Quality's recent Task Force on Land Use and Urban Growth have recommended at least extending the option of requiring assessments for private projects at the local level. *The strong likelihood of a virtually universal requirement suggests that project proponents gain little by fleeing to those few localities not yet caught up in the environmental surge.*

ALTERNATIVE CONTENTS AND FORMATS

Impact assessment requirements do vary among the cities, counties, and states which require them. In most instances, however, the variations are superficial ones reflecting particular local concerns. All environmental assessment regulations trace their lineage from the same venerable antecedent—the National Environmental Policy Act of 1969. (Pub. L. 91-190, 42 U.S.C. 4321 et seq.) NEPA, therefore, provides a good starting point for the person who wants to decide what to include in a report. Interestingly, NEPA differs from some of its scions because of the very definition of the term "environment." The federal definition, far broader than many of its followers, emphasizes the *total* human environment, rather than limiting consideration to primarily natural physical factors. The NEPA format is described in section 102(2)(C) of the 1969 National Environmental Policy Act and exhibit 3-1. The format requires coverage of five specific points, in addition to a description of present conditions and the proposed action:

1. The probable environmental impact of the proposed action;

2. Any adverse environmental effects which cannot be avoided should the proposal be implemented;

3. Alternatives to the proposed action;

4. The relationship between local short term uses of man's environment and the maintenance and enhancement of long term productivity; and,

5. Any irreversible and irretrievable commitments of resources which would be involved in the proposed action should it be implemented.

Although not specifically identified in the initial guidelines issued by the Council on Environmental Quality (the NEPA "handbook"), two other items introduced in the California Environmental Quality Act are implied by NEPA and explicitly stated in many of its more recent progeny:

6. Mitigation measures; and,

7. Growth inducing impacts.

The burgeoning environmental literature has suggested scores of specific formats for the environmental analyses broadly outlined in the 1969 act. Jens Sorensen and Mitchell Moss of the University of California,[1] for example, suggested the following three-stage process:

1. Identify the environmental, social, and economic conditions that may be changed by the project;

2. Predict the intensity and spatial dimensions of the changes likely to occur; and

Exhibit 3-1.

BASIC NEPA EIS FRAMEWORK

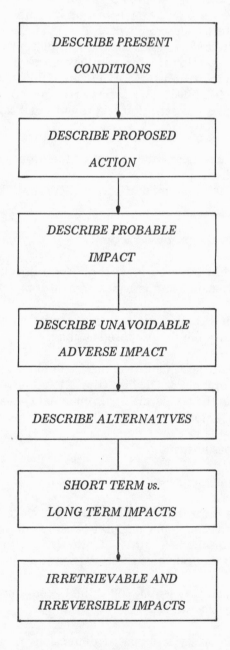

Source: Section 102(2)(C) of the 1969 National Environmental Policy Act.

3. Evaluate the costs and benefits of the condition changes in terms of its costs and benefits to different groups of society.

Lewis Hopkins, *et al.*,[2] of the University of Illinois have objected to environmental impact documentation that follows in exact order the five section NEPA format. They argue that subsections 1 and 2, referring to impacts and adverse effects respectively, cannot be discussed before alternative strategies (subsection 3) are evaluated. They further reason that there is little difference between subsections 1 and 2 (environmental impact and adverse environmental effect), and they mention other similar drawbacks. The major thrust of their criticism is that a statement that directly follows the NEPA format will be ambiguous and logically deficient. Instead Hopkins, *et al.*, suggest the following format:

1. Describe present conditions;

2. Describe alternative actions;

3. Describe probable impacts of each alternative by relating the expected future conditions to present conditions;

4. Identify the alternative chosen and indicate the evaluation which led to choice;

5. Describe probable impacts of proposed action in detail; and

6. Describe techniques to be used to minimize harm.

This strategy is outlined in exhibit 3-2.

Richard N. L. Andrews[3] follows up Hopkins' reasoning and makes the point more incisively: "Collecting disproportionate amounts of data on a single proposed action has little relationship to the task of reducing uncertainties in the decision process, and it adds nothing to the quality of the decision between that action and alternatives to it, since there are no comparable data on the alternatives to illuminate the tradeoffs. It is far more important to use resources to bring out detailed comparison of alternatives than to use them for exhaustive documentation after tentatively choosing a single course of action." Unfortunately, neither Hopkins nor Andrews understands or appreciates the development process and its influence on EIS filings. Land is zoned for certain uses, thus restricting significantly (although not eliminating) the range of alternatives applicable to a particular site. Those who hold land and move to the point of development have basic development capacities which further limit alternatives. The NEPA format, with all of its shortcomings, may yet be the wisest of all.

Numerous other approaches for preparing environmental impact statements have been suggested. One approach recommended by James A. Roberts Associates, Inc., California consultants,[4] is shown in exhibit 3-3. Another suggested by Gail Hemenway in a report for the Associated Home Builders of the Greater East Bay (California)[5] is displayed in exhibit 3-4.

Many governmental agencies have added to the proliferation of recommendations by issuing their own guidelines on EIS format. The Department of Housing and Urban Development,[6] for example, recommends this format:

1. Describe the proposed project;

2. Describe the existing environment;

3. Discuss the impact *of* the environment on project design and the development's residents and users;

4. Evaluate the impact of the project *on* the environment;

5. Discuss *internal* project environment (for large developments, such as New Towns);

6. Discuss alternatives to the proposed project;

7. Discuss short and long term impacts of the project;

8. Note actions taken by the developer and/or governmental agencies to mitigate the impact of the project on the environment; and

9. Describe official and private reaction to the proposed development.

CONTENTS AND FORMAT OF THIS HANDBOOK

Obviously, no single format has yet been established for preparing environmental impact statements. This is not surprising because environmental review is still in its infancy, in a period of flux. Additionally, given the environmental writers' continued emphasis that review be flexible, it is unlikely that any *one* rigid approach for all development, under all conditions, will ever be required.

Keeping in mind this framework of flexibility, what is one possible approach for evaluating the environmental impact of residential projects? This handbook argues that EIS review cannot completely wean itself away from the basic guidelines outlined by NEPA, (See exhibit 3-1.) It also maintains that, given HUD's significant role in housing production, this agency's outline must also be given special prominence. Finally, the handbook gives primary attention to the needs of developers, public officials who receive their plans, and environmental groups who attempt to preserve

EXHIBIT 3-2.
PROPOSED OUTLINE FOR AN ENVIRONMENTAL IMPACT STATEMENT: LEWIS HOPKINS, ET AL.

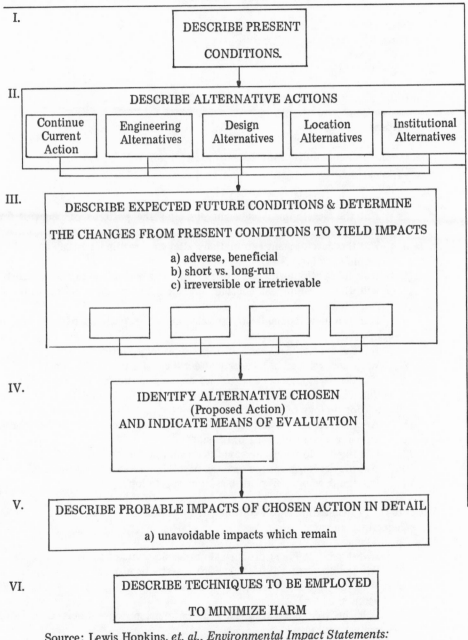

I. DESCRIBE PRESENT CONDITIONS.

II. DESCRIBE ALTERNATIVE ACTIONS

Continue Current Action | Engineering Alternatives | Design Alternatives | Location Alternatives | Institutional Alternatives

III. DESCRIBE EXPECTED FUTURE CONDITIONS & DETERMINE THE CHANGES FROM PRESENT CONDITIONS TO YIELD IMPACTS

a) adverse, beneficial
b) short vs. long-run
c) irreversible or irretrievable

IV. IDENTIFY ALTERNATIVE CHOSEN
(Proposed Action)
AND INDICATE MEANS OF EVALUATION

V. DESCRIBE PROBABLE IMPACTS OF CHOSEN ACTION IN DETAIL

a) unavoidable impacts which remain

VI. DESCRIBE TECHNIQUES TO BE EMPLOYED TO MINIMIZE HARM

Source: Lewis Hopkins, *et. al.*, *Environmental Impact Statements: A Handbook for Writers and Reviewers*, Chicago, Illinois, Institute for Environmental Quality, 1973, \
Distributed by National Technical Information Service
Order Number PB-226-276, August 1973.

EXHIBIT 3-3
SUGGESTED CONTENTS FOR ENVIRONMENTAL IMPACT STATEMENTS:
JAMES A. ROBERTS ASSOCIATES, INC.

I. Description of project area
  A.   General location
  B.   Present uses
  C.   Legal description

II. What is the description and purpose of the development?
  A.   Description
  B.   Purpose

III. What are the probable impacts on the natural environment?
  A.   General statement
  B.   Specific questions
    1.   Is the development controversial?
    2.   Will the development substantially alter the patterns of behavior for mammals?
    3.   Will the development substantially alter the breeding, nesting, or feeding grounds for birds?
    4.   Will the development substantially alter the patterns of behavior of fish?
    5.   Will the development substantially alter the patterns of behavior of amphibians or reptiles?
    6.   Will the development substantially alter the patterns of behavior of insects?
    7.   Will the development cause or increase water pollution?
    8.   Will the development adversely affect the water table in the area?
    9.   Will the development cause or increase air pollution?
    10. Will the development increase the stability or instability of the soils and/or geology of the site?
    11. Are the geologic or soils conditions of the site hazardous to continuous human occupance on-site or off-site?
    12. Will the development increase the erosion potential of the site?
    13. Will the development increase the potential fire hazards of the site?
    14. Will the development disturb existing vegetation?

IV. What are the probable impacts on cultural environments?
  A.   General statement
  B.   Specific questions
    1.   Will the development produce abnormal amounts of traffic?
    2.   Will the development have significant aesthetic effects?
    3.   Will the development divide or disrupt existing land uses (including economic base)?
    4.   Will the development destroy or have deleterious effects on existing recreational uses?
    5.   Will the development affect areas of unique interest or beauty (including archaeology and/or anthropology)?

V. Are there probable adverse environmental effects which cannot be avoided?

EXHIBIT 3-3
SUGGESTED CONTENTS FOR ENVIRONMENTAL IMPACT STATEMENTS:
JAMES A. ROBERTS ASSOCIATES, INC. (Continued)

A.   Natural
B.   Cultural

VI. What environmental monitoring programs are needed?
   A.   Water Quality
   B.   Erosion
   C.   Vegetation (including fire hazard)
   D.   Air quality
   E.   Wildlife

VII. What alternatives exist to the proposed development?

VIII. What is the relationship of the development to the long-term goals for regional development?

IX. What are the growth inducing factors of the proposed development?

X. What problems or objections have been raised by local, state, and federal agencies?

XI. What are the growth inducing factors of the proposed development?

Source: James A. Roberts Associates, Inc., Sacramento, California

EXHIBIT 3-4
SUGGESTED CONTENTS FOR ENVIRONMENTAL IMPACT STATEMENTS:
GAIL HEMENWAY

1. *Project Description and Purpose*
A. Proposal
  1. Area
  2. Density
  3. Open Space
  4. Dwelling Units by Type
  5. Breakdown on Housing Units
B. Purpose
C. History of Area

2. *Environmental Impact of Proposed Project*
A. General Description of Area Affected (Surrounding Land Uses)
B. Soil Conditions
C. Natural Hazards
  1. Flood Plains
  2. Seismic Damage
  3. Unstable Areas
D. Natural Factors
  1. Existing Vegetation
  2. Wildlife
  3. Agriculture Use
  4. Climate
  5. Mean Annual Precipitation
E. Existing Pollution
  1. Noise
  2. Air
  3. Water or Sewage
F. Public Facilities (Impact of Proposed Project on Public Facilities)
  1. Transportation Congestion
  2. Traffic Congestion

3. *Adverse Environmental Effects which Cannot be Avoided*
A. Excessive Cuts and Fills, Grating, etc.
B. Destruction of Natural Features
  1. Trees
  2. Wildlife
  3. Natural Creeks
  4. Elimination of Existing Housing
  5. Future Zoning

4. *Alternatives to Proposed Projects*
A. Minimizing Adverse Effects by Re-Designing
B. Shielding to Reduce Noise Pollution
C. Other Land Used than Proposed

5. *Short Run/Long Run Relationships*
A. Disruption during Construction
B. Destruction of Vegetation, Wildlife, etc., or Alterations of Natural Features

EXHIBIT 3-4 (Continued)
SUGGESTED CONTENTS FOR ENVIRONMENTAL IMPACT STATEMENTS:
GAIL HEMENWAY

3. Schools
4. Utilities
   a. Water
   b. Sewage
   c. Gas & Electric
   d. Telephone
   e. Fire, etc.
G. Aesthetics
   1. View
      Restrictions
   2. Landscaping
   3. Project
      Aesthetics

Source: Gail D. Hemenway, *Developers Handbook-Environmental Impact Statements*, Berkeley, Calif., Associated Home Builders of the Greater East Bay, Inc., 1973.

EXHIBIT 3-5. EIS DATA COMPONENT INDEX

PROJECT ENVIRONMENTAL SUBSECTIONS	I Project Description	II Existing Environment	III Impact of/on Environment	IV Internal Environment	V Alternatives	VI Unavoidable Adverse Impact	VII Impacts Over Time	VIII Irreversible/ Irretrievable Commitment
PURPOSE OF THE PROJECT	I.A.							
STATUS OF THE PROJECT	I.B.							
LOCATION OF THE PROJECT	I.C							
PHYSICAL ENVIRONMENT								
Land and Climate		II.A.	III.A.	IV.A.		VI.A.		
Soils		II.A.1.	III.A.1.					
Topography		II.A.1.1.	III.A.1.1.					
Subsurface Conditions		II.A.1.2.	III.A.1.2.					
Special Conditions		II.A.1.3.	III.A.1.3.					
Climate		II.A.1.4.	III.A.1.4.					
Vegetation and Wildlife		II.A.1.5.	III.A.1.5.					
Land Use		II.A.2.	III.A.2.					
Infrastructure		II.A.3.	III.A.3.					
Water Supply		II.A.4.	III.A.4.					
Sewage		II.A.4.1.	III.A.4.1.					
Solid Waste		II.A.4.2.	III.A.4.2.					
Drainage		II.A.4.3.	III.A.4.3.					
Energy		II.A.4.4.	III.A.4.4.					
Transportation		II.A.4.5.	III.A.4.5.					
Air Pollution		II.A.4.6.	III.A.4.6.					
Noise Pollution		II.A.5.	III.A.5.					
Water Pollution		II.A.6.	III.A.6.					
Other		II.A.7.	III.A.7.					
		II.A.8.	III.A.8.					
SOCIAL ENVIRONMENT		II.B.	III.B.	IV.B.		VI.B.		
Community Facilities		II.B.1.	III.B.1.					
School		II.B.1.1.	III.B.1.1.					
Public Safety–Health		II.B.1.2.	III.B.1.2.					
Recreation and Culture		II.B.1.3.	III.B.1.3.					
Employment		II.B.2.	III.B.2.					
Socioeconomic Characteristics	II.B.3.	III.B.3.						
Other		II.B.4.	III.B.4.					

PROJECT-ENVIRONMENTAL SECTIONS

EXHIBIT 3-5. EIS DATA COMPONENT INDEX (Continued)

PROJECT ENVIRONMENTAL SUBSECTIONS	I Project Description	II Existing Environment	III Impact of/on Environment	IV Internal Environment	V Alternatives	VI Unavoidable Adverse Impact	VII Impacts Over Time	VIII Irreversible/ Irretrievable Commitment
AESTHETIC ENVIRONMENT		II.C.	III.C.	IV.C.		VI.C. VI.D. VI.D.1. VI.D.2. VI.D.3.		
MITIGATIVE ACTIONS								
Developer								
Governmental								
Private								
ALTERNATIVES					V			
ALTERNATIVES' ADVERSE IMPACT						VI.E.		
CONSTRUCTION								
PHASE IMPACT							VII.A.	
SHORT TERM IMPACT							VII.B.	
LONG TERM IMPACT							VII.C.	
IRREVERSIBLE/ IRRETRIEVABLE COMMITMENT								VIII

PROJECT-ENVIRONMENTAL SECTIONS

natural resources in their development path. This handbook, therefore, proposes a format that *combines* NEPA's and HUD's guidelines as follows:

SECTION I—Describe the proposed project, including its purpose (subsection I.A), status (subsection I.B), and location (subsection I.C). (Adopted from section E of the HUD guidelines.)

SECTION II—Describe the existing environment of the site and area, including physical features (subsection II.A), social characteristics (subsection II.B), and aesthetic nature (subsection II.C). (Adopted from section F of the HUD guidelines.)

SECTION III—Discuss the impact of the environment on the project's development and design and on the project's residents and users. Include effect of physical (subsection III.A), social(subsection III.B), and aesthetic (subsection III.C) environments. (Adopted from subsection I of NEPA, section 102(2)(C) and HUD guidelines section G.)
—Also describe the impact of the project on the physical, social, and aesthetic environments (subsections III.A, III.B, and III.C, respectively). Where possible, discuss precisely what will be affected and the nature of the effect, in terms of its source, its severity, its duration, and its scope. Use quantitative measures whenever they are reliable, for example projected carbon monoxide levels, or population density; also consider qualitative measures such as the relative importance of the environmental factor in light of national or local values. Discuss measures taken by the developer and others to minimize the effect, and the relationship of the environmental impact (and mitigative measures) to official and area-wide planning. (Adopted from NEPA section 102(2)(C), subsection I and HUD sections H and L.)

SECTION IV—Describe the internal *physical (subsection IV.A), social (subsection IV.B), and aesthetic (subsection IV.C) environments of large developments, such as New Towns. (Adopted from HUD section I.)*

SECTION V—Describe alternatives to the proposed action, such as limited or reduced construction, conventional development, or construction on another site. (Adopted from NEPA section 102(2)(C), subsection III.)

SECTION VI—Describe adverse environmental effects which cannot be avoided should the proposal be implemented. Include physical (subsection VI.A), social (subsection VI.B), and aesthetic (subsection VI.C) impacts. Also discuss actions taken by the developer or governmental agencies which will mitigate the environmental damage (subsection VI.D). The last subsection should summarize the discussions in section III on mitigative activities. Such analysis is not redundant because it creates a proper perspective for reviewing the unavoidable environmental impact. Discuss also environmental impacts of the project which could have been avoided were one of the alternatives adopted, adverse impacts of the projects which could not be avoided by any alternative, and adverse impacts which were avoided by choosing the recommended action (subsection VI.E). (Adopted from NEPA section 102(2)(C) subsection II and HUD section K.)

SECTION VII—Describe the relationship between local short term uses of the environment and maintenance and enhancement of long term productivity. Discuss effects during the construction phase (subsection VII.A) as well as short and long term impacts (subsections VII.B and VII.C, respectively). (Adopted from NEPA Section 102(2)(C) subsection IV.)

SECTION VIII—Describe any irreversible and irretrievable commitment of resources which would be made if the proposed actions were implemented. (Adopted from NEPA section 102(2)(C) subsection V.)

A schema of the format sections by subject is shown in exhibit 3-5. A detailed description of the content for each element of the environmental impact statement is given in chapter 6, EIS Guidelines.

INTERPRETATION

EIS interpretation can be more important than content and format. If the developer/applicant has misinterpreted what is to be presented, neither the scope nor the form of the EIS will be sufficient to rectify its misdirection.

To begin, references will be made to *significant* impacts, as distinguished from ordinary effects. The distinction is important because in many jurisdictions an environmental assessment is not required *unless* the project's impacts will be significant.[7] (For a more detailed discussion of significance, see chapter 4, EIS Review Process, and Appendix B, EIS in the Courts.) The *magnitude* of impact is often quantifiable (in terms such as the number of households displaced or the number of trees removed) and is usually much easier to assess than its significance. Many consultants who prepare reports for both project proponents and local agencies feel that any attempt to identify significance, in fact, removes the assessment process from the realm of objectivity. Since an assessment is supposed to enable decisions which would ultimately enhance the quality of the environment and the definition of environmental quality varies widely, a value judgment appears inescapable. Moreover, local policy-makers sometimes forget just what it is that they are supposed to be trying to accomplish. In such cases reference to the locally acknowledged value system (in the form of the master plan) and its policies may help to demonstrate that the significance of the proposal is its very support of adopted local objectives!

Another frequent area of confusion is the distinction between *alternatives* and *mitigation* measures. The discussion of alternatives should include *other uses* for the site which would serve objectives different from the primary ones sought by the proponent, as well as *other sites* where a similar project serving the same objectives could occur. *Alternatives* to a proposed shopping center would, therefore, include development of the site for single family housing or a community park, as well as other locations where a shopping center aimed at the same market could be constructed or perhaps a center is not needed at all. Obviously, this clarification of the "alternative" definition could play havoc with the master plan and its regulatory expression, extant zoning.

Mitigation measures, on the other hand, are ways to reduce the negative effects which have been identified. Every mitigation measure must, therefore, be matched with an impact. The impact statement, for example, might suggest eliminating windows on the residential frontages on a major thoroughfare as a mitigative action to reduce noise. In this case, the impact section should include an analysis of existing and projected traffic levels on that thoroughfare. While an attempt should be made to identify measures to reduce all of the undesirable changes listed, some changes will be unavoidable. For this reason, one of the alternatives listed should always be the alternative of no project at all.

Of course, other changes might take place if no project at all is undertaken and these may be far more undesirable than any which would result from the project as proposed. (Failure to approve a particular residential development, for example, could result in construction of an office building which would generate twice as much automobile traffic.) Developers who try to sweeten their proposals by suggesting far-fetched and perhaps costly steps for reducing adverse impacts should be aware that local agencies are paying increasing attention to their pipe dreams. Some agencies are even beginning to impose suggested measures as conditions of project approval. While the redesign of site plans to ensure that no structure faces a noisy street may be a reasonable enough condition, developers should think twice before suggesting electric cars to reduce reliance on pollution-causing combustion engines or expensive compacting equipment to solve solid waste disposal problems.

The relationship between *short term uses* and *long term productivity* is sometimes viewed as a requirement to justify decisions to future generations. Why is the action justified at this time in view of its potential adverse effects? Will a delay in carrying out the project reduce negative impacts? Moreover, why is this location the best one for carrying out the project's stated objectives. Once again, those preparing and reviewing reports would do well to refer to the adopted goals and policies of the local agency. A city with a recognized need for low-cost housing, yet limited vacant residentially-zoned land, would be hard put to justify approval of yet expensive subdivision.

The fifth NEPA requirement—"a description of resources which, once committed to the project will forever after be lost for other purposes"—is often misunderstood. Construction materials used in a building project are not the only resources irreversibly committed when a project is undertaken. Neither will tearing down a freeway return the setting to its original state. Try instead to view the project as the first in a chain of occurrences which, once started, cannot be broken.

With the newfound interest in *growth* as a unique phenomenon responsible for a raft of environmental and fiscal ills, it was not surprising that California decided to require special consideration of this factor. In fact, although no specific reference to growth is made in NEPA, even the earliest federal guidelines required discussion of the ultimate consequences of an action for population distribution and concentration, and the second-level effects that population changes could have on natural resources and public services. It may be helpful, therefore, to think of growth-induced impacts simply as long-range changes which may result from population changes directly related to the proposal. The project itself may not directly cause further development to occur, but will either reduce barriers that impede it or provide reasons to justify it. In many cases the key to determining the type of growth effect which may result is an understanding of the project's impact on the state of public finances. A new subdivision in an area with little in the way of existing public services (sewage treatment capacity, for example) may well necessitate expensive capital outlays requiring the sale of bonds or the levying of additional assessments. To reduce the financial burden per household, additional residential development is encouraged, resulting in the need for yet more services.

Frequently, impact statements limit their coverage to only those public facilities and services for which the local agency approving the proposal is directly responsible. By eliminating highway improvements (paid for by taxes and state and federal grants), for example, a project's net financial impact could be beneficial. Since community groups may well be reviewing the impact statement and the taxpayer is ultimately the one who pays the tariff, public costs should be included even if they don't come out of the city's coffers. The question of *specificity* remains. Even if each item required in the local ordinance is dutifully given passing reference, an impact statement may still be found inadequate because of the level of detail included. Consider the following description of probable impact on wildlife systems taken from a report submitted to a Bay Area county:

> As in other rural areas of . . . County, the usual species of California bird and wildlife can be seen from time to time in the project area. Construction of the 45 homes will cause most of these species to move further back into the hills and farm areas.

There is no rule of thumb—for instance, 10 pages per $100,000 investment—to determine how detailed an impact statement should be.

Moreover, there probably shouldn't be, because depending on its location, the same project can be extraordinarily significant or of minimal import. There are a few methods, however, that can be used to gauge the kind of attention to detail which will be expected by the statement's audience. In some cases these clues are obvious. A report for a project in an area recognized for its natural or man-made aesthetic qualities should devote greater attention to aesthetics than would ordinarily be the case. Even though earthquakes have been known to occur in New Jersey, seismic considerations would rarely be treated in the section on soil characteristics. In California, on the other hand, information on how particular types of soil will act in the event of an earthquake is of major importance. The local agency should be able to provide copies of reports for previous projects which will help to determine the kind of detail expected. Finally, early consultation with the kinds of agencies and organizations referred to earlier can be most informative. Some of the questions to ask would include:

1. Have there been recent proposals in this locale which have encountered problems? What kind of concerns were raised?

2. Have projects *of this type* been recently proposed?

3. In general, what kinds of issues have been of interest in the community? Conversion of agriculture? Industrial noise? Shortage of lower-cost housing?

In smaller towns, the local newspaper's clip files can often provide valuable clues to community concerns. The planning staff in larger cities should also be able to alert a project proponent to precedents.

CONCLUSION

This section has outlined a content and format for environmental impact statements that can guide the writer or reviewer. This outline was derived from carefully reviewing the basic NEPA statutes, governmental agency guidelines, and scores of EIS reports. We wish to stress, however, that there is no single EIS format appropriate for all projects in all communities. Rather, our recommendations should be viewed as a basic guide to be modified as local conditions dictate.

NOTES

1. Jens C. Sorensen and Mitchell L. Moss, *Procedures and Programs to Assist in the Environmental Impacts Statement,* published jointly by the University of California and the University of Southern California and distributed by the California Marine Advisory Programs, April 1973.

2. Lewis Hopkins, *et al., Environmental Impact Statements: A Handbook for Writers and Reviewers,*

Chicago, Ill., Institute for Environmental Quality, 1973. Distributed by National Technical Information Service, Order Number PB-226-276, August 1973.

3. Richard N. L. Andrews, "A Philosophy of Environmental Impact Assessment," *Journal of Soil and Water Conservation*, Vol. 28, 1973, p. 200.

4. James A. Roberts Associates, Inc., Sacramento, California. This firm has been extremely active in the environmental assessment field.

5. Gail D. Hemenway, *Developer's Handbook—Environmental Impact Statements*, Berkeley, California, Associated Home Builders of the Greater East Bay, Inc., 1973.

6. *Federal Register*, Vol. 39, No. 37, February 22, 1974, p. 6824.

7. Usually jurisdictions that require an EIS when the project's expected impacts are significant have specified thresholds which guide the applicant and reviewer in making this determination.

INTRODUCTION

The object of this section of the handbook is to describe what a developer/applicant may expect when he files an environmental impact statement at the local level. Who reviews the document, how long does the filing process take, what are the line and staff relationships affecting the proposal, and what happens when multiple levels of review come to bear on a single action?

Obviously the review process varies according to the type of legislation that exists at the state level and the specific ordinance structure in effect locally. In this handbook, examples from the Northeast and West will be used to supplement national generalizations.

As noted earlier, knowing who *may* review your environmental impact assessment is sometimes more important than knowing who *must* review it. All too often, citizens' groups are far more attentive to project details than are disinterested elected officials or overburdened staff. Once a local conservationist brings significant information to the attention of the staff or officials, however, they may be reluctant to proceed with the project until it has been subjected to more intensive review. Nevertheless, since it is the policy group that has to take the statutory action which will make or break your EIS, it is still helpful to understand what types of staff and policy-makers are likely to come into contact with it at some time during processing.

Although practices vary among the many jurisdictions across the country, in most instances the determination of whether a report will be required and the informal but *substantive* review once it is actually prepared will occur at the staff level. The formal review and adoption or approval of the document is virtually always the responsibility of a policy body.

The policy body most likely to be involved in the review and approval is the Planning Commission. In a significant number of communities, however, the review of environmental impact statements has become the responsibility of a special committee or board usually composed of elected officials and interested citizens.

At the staff level, an environmental commission or an interdepartmental committee including representatives of the planning, public works, buildings, and health departments may perform the preliminary review and determine the necessity for report preparation. If a single person is responsible for overseeing the whole process, more often than not that person will be the planning director. In some larger cities and counties, a separate position of environmental officer or environmental planner has been created. In still others, the planning director has simply assumed an additional title along with the extra work.

In order to provide a general idea of how the system works, we will follow a project through the review process in a hypothetical city. We will assume that at the state level there is a requirement that local political subdivisions consider the environmental impact of actions they seek to undertake or approve; even the smallest cities then, through enabling legislation have the right to adopt EIS and review procedures.

The opening of the local ordinance frequently states that we must recognize that (a) "man's actions have a prolonged and inexcusable effect upon the natural resources of the town and on the organic and inorganic animal and human systems dependent on those resources," (b) in order to assure the public health and welfare, the development growth of local entities must be synchronized with available natural resources, and (c) the locality through its governmental actions, specifically its zoning, land use, and permit granting activities, has the responsibility and authority to assure a healthful, safe, and pleasing environment for present and future residents.

The standard ordinance issues a statement of local policy (for example, that requested permits and certificates of occupancy will be conditional upon EIS approval); states when an EIS will be required; details the topical areas the EIS must address; outlines the required review procedures, including review records and required public hearings; and closes with a discussion of filing fees.

To mitigate somewhat the "taking" issue, the local ordinance may also specify that the EIS requirements are not intended to cause unreasonable delay in the regular processing of applications for permits or other types of approval. In concert with the process described here, therefore, is the regular clearance to which any application requiring a planning decision is submitted and the preparation of any other supporting documentation which may be required.

THE OPTIONAL PREAPPLICATION CONFERENCE

While usually not specifically required, a meeting with planning department staff to cover the ground rules before an EIS is prepared can save a good deal of time later on. Points to be covered would normally include the extent and emphasis of the EIS to be submitted to the agency and anticipated timing and fees. The planning department is also a good source for information on likely conflicts, related projects and the type of concerns local officials have been known to express. An early public hearing to ascertain local feelings is also worth considering.

In the Planned Unit Development literature, the preapplication conference associated with the PUD filing process has been gaining increased importance. Even though the filing procedure is spelled out in detail, a face-to-face encounter and initial discussion has been found to be of utmost importance in determining PUD filing emphases. The same situation extends to EIS filings. What aspects of the numerous elements of the EIS application are important to the local review board? Have any other applications been submitted for essentially the same geographic area from which information may be obtained? An ounce of preapplication EIS intelligence is worth a pound of subsequent EIS filing material!

IS AN EIS NECESSARY?

Two basic criteria for filing environmental impact statements confront the developer at the local level. The simplest, most arbitrary, and most frequent is a threshold criterion above which an EIS *must* be filed (for example, for subdivisions of five or more acres, eleven lots, ten housing units, etc.). In this case the determination is quite simple, and the developer knows his status almost immediately.

The other case, derived from the federal and California experience, involves a more complex definition of environmental significance to determine whether or not there will be an acknowledged environmental impact and thus the requirement to file. (For HUD's requirements at the federal level see Addendum A-1 and A-2 to this section.) In this latter case an environmental clearance is issued after a checklist is submitted by the developer/applicant and reviewed by the environmental officer, planning director, environmental commission, or a multidisciplinary staff committee.

This second procedure—thumbnail sketch, to finding, to EIS, if necessary—is much less arbitrary and eliminates small projects from submitting full blown EIS's or even large projects from willing submission of an EIS, when one aspect of its impact is glaring. (In Addendum B-1, 2 to this section, the thumbnail sketch is planned out more fully using HUD format as an example.)

This abbreviated checklist to provide the thumbnail sketch may cover the following areas:

A. Project identification.
B. Compliance with applicable standards and plans.
C. Impact of the environment (site suitability).
   1. slope stability
   2. foundation conditions

3. terrain
4. soil permeability
5. ground water
6. natural hazards
7. man-made hazards
8. nuisances
9. compatibility of use and scale
10. neighborhood character
11. elementary schools
12. junior high schools
13. employment
14. shopping
15. park playground and open space
16. police and fire
17. health care and social services
18. transportation
19. other services
20. utilities
D. Impact on the environment (environmental suitability).
   1. geological features or resources
   2. rock and soil stability
   3. soil erodability
   4. ground water
   5. open streams and lakes
   6. plant and animal life
   7. energy resources
   8. social fabric and community structures
   9. displacement of individuals or family
   10. aesthetics and urban design
   11. existing or planned community facilities
E. A brief summary of the issues of C & D.
F. A discussion of how impact of project interacts with other anticipated or planned development.
H. Location and market (See HUD Handbooks 4150.1 and 4465.1).
I. Derive an environmental finding.

This is the type of format used in the pre-EIS environmental review process and has a rather standard set of procedures associated with it. In effect, it is a brief glimpse at the type, magnitude, and location of a project to determine the potential *significance* of its impact, with an aim to screen those projects requiring an EIS from those not needing to file.

The first type of examination that must take place as a part of the review process is a determination of the "existing environmental situation." Among the questions commonly considered are: what do trends hold for an area in terms of environmental impact *without* the project? What are the environmental conditions which exist prior to the project, unaffected by its implementation?

The next procedure that should be completed is a brief sketch of likely environmental impacts occasioned by the project, together with a gross estimation of the magnitude of these impacts.

The third procedure is to attempt to determine whether or not changes can be made either within the project or on the environment to eliminate or minimize identified impacts. A brief discussion of alternatives (sites, site design, project or no project, etc.) also should be included in this stage.

The fourth step of the review process is to come up with a finding on the project's environmental impact based on the previous analyses. The finding should consider whether a project *is* or *is not* a "major action significantly affecting the quality of the human environment."

The fifth step is the issuance of an environmental clearance, that is, determining whether the project actually requires an environmental impact statement. Notice of intent to file or not to file an EIS should be made to the public through local media, environmental groups, local and state agencies, and the appropriate A-95 clearinghouse.

The pre-EIS review process, depending upon the size and scope of the project, may take 30 days; frequently the public is given 15 days to comment if there is an intent not to file an EIS and the same period of time before the scheduling of a preliminary public meeting, should the preparation of an EIS be deemed necessary.

If an EIS is required, the next consideration is whether public meetings will be scheduled early in EIS preparation (prior to the applicant's filing of his proposal) or after the EIS has been completed, to be aired publicly in concert with the project proposal. Obviously there is no set answer here. The same type of considerations pertain to the *scheduling* of public hearings and the holding of public hearings at all. Factors to consider are the size and cost of the project, the degree of local interest, the complexity of issues, and the extent to which the public has been informed via other means.

THE FORMAL EIS REVIEW PROCESS

Once an EIS is determined to be necessary, its submission to municipal agencies consists of several steps. The first is the formal submission of the "draft EIS" and attendant site plan application to whomever is designated to receive it locally; in the Northeast, this is either the planning or zoning board. (This serves notice to both developer and municipality that the clock indicating filing time has begun.)

Once submitted, a basic check of the draft EIS's completeness is undertaken usually by a subcommittee of the planning board or the local environmental commission.

The third step is a report by the committee evaluating the document's completeness, after circulation to the township engineer, building inspector, health inspector, and municipal planning consultants (if any).

The fourth step is frequently a resubmission of the reworked EIS to the township planning board, county planning board, and state planning/environmental agencies by the applicant.

At all levels the final draft is circulated to interested public agencies and private groups for comment and additional review. Frequently at this time an informal, informational public hearing is scheduled by the environmental commission on the final EIS submission.

Next a formal public hearing is held on both the site plan application and final EIS. Reports are heard from the township engineer, building inspector, health inspector, municipal planning consultants, county and state officials, and the general public. Revisions may be made to the report by the public agency in response to substantive comments issued during the public hearings. Ultimately a decision is made by the municipality to reject the project, approve, or approve conditionally.

An additional 30 to 45 day review period is frequent, but it is not unusual for extensions to be granted if a project has generated a considerable amount of controversy or if comments by reviewers indicate major gaps in the EIS. In addition, even if the EIS is approved, the *project's* approval may be delayed if the EIS has uncovered unanticipated problems about the project's impact on the community, which require solution before the planning board will render a decision.

What kind of comments are likely to be raised during the review period? First of all, developers should be aware that the most cogent and incisive questions are often asked by citizens with no formal training in planning, engineering, or municipal finance, but who have an abiding interest in their community's future and their own tax bills. The topics covered in a six-page letter one Bay Area resident wrote in response to an EIS for a major residential development in her community included neighborhood density, bonding capacity to finance required capital expenditures, availability of water supply, and the cost and source of funds for expanding sewage treatment and transportation facilities. Other residents questioned the availability of gas tax funds to finance necessary traffic improvements and the accuracy of the developer's statements regarding the school district's intention to construct needed classrooms. Other California agencies commenting on the report included: the local utility district; an adjoining city; the County public works and planning departments; the State Departments of Transportation and Fish and Game, the State Air Resources Board, and the Council of Governments and regional transportation agency.

THE ENVIRONMENTAL REVIEW RECORD

Documentation of the process leading to the determination that an EIS is required or not and to the ultimate filing of the EIS is a necessary precaution. Comments on the project's movement through the review process are essential if the developer/applicant, private citizens, public funding agencies, or the courts question the determination made at a particular juncture of review.

The record should contain:

(a) A description of the project
(b) Documentation of the review process as set forth earlier
(c) A description of the existing environmental conditions the environmental impacts identified, and modifications/changes made to compensate for environmental impacts
(d) The environmental finding
(e) The environmental clearance granted
(f) A copy of the EIS, if required

Input from the local planner and environmental groups, minutes of the planning board or environmental commission meetings, and facts from the developer/applicant may be used to compile the record along the basic guidelines of this format.

THE REVIEW AND EIS REQUIREMENTS OF THE PUBLIC SECTOR

Background
In the event that the developer is seeking some level of public assistance from the traditional source in housing, the Department of Housing and Urban Development (HUD), the basic format and procedures of the inclusive guidelines pertain. However there are HUD forms which must be initiated.

To capsulize the history of its involvement—the Department of Housing and Urban Development is involved *directly* with environmental impact at the federal level with a stated policy "to reject proposals which have unacceptable environmental impacts based on HUD environmental policies and standards, which cannot be avoided, and to encourage modification of project proposals or plans in order to enhance environmental quality and minimize environmental harm."

At the federal level, HUD's Assistant Secretary for Community Planning and Development (CPD) is responsible for coordinating departmentwide aspects of environmental policies and procedures. An environmental clearance officer (ECO) within the Federal Insurance Administration, the New Communities Administration, and the Federal Disaster Assistance Administration is required to develop standards and procedures for EIS, maintain a reference file of background and resource material, monitor proposed policy actions and maintain liaison with the Assistant Secretary for CPD.

Within the regional offices, environmental clearance officers (ECO's) perform similar reference and resource gathering functions and also are required to maintain a list of all environmental impact statements which are being prepared within HUD auspices.

For non-Title I Community Development or 701 Planning Assistance activities, any HUD action that might be deemed a major action significantly affecting the quality of the human environment is subject to potential EIS scrutiny at the federal level. This involves such actions as property dispositions, disaster relief or new communities' activities.

The Levels of Clearance

A definite environmental clearance process has been set up by HUD at the federal level which involves a three-level clearance not dissimilar from the two step (thumbnail sketch and EIS) procedure recommended previously. While this procedure is subject to change, it does provide the handbook user with an example of HUD's reactions to EIS filings. The three levels are (a) normal environmental clearance, (b) special environmental clearance, and (c) environmental impact statement clearance. Normal clearance is essentially a consistency check with HUD environmental policies and standards, and a brief evaluation of environmental impact. A normal clearance typically is required for multifamily housing, public housing, college housing, mobile homes, or Section 8 Housing Assistance Payments of 5 to 199 units, less than 200-bed hospitals or nursing homes, or any proposal processed as a subdivision. Obviously there are other categories of actions that fall within normal clearance procedures; however these same examples, for efficiency and clarity, will be used throughout.

Special clearance requires an environmental evaluation of greater detail and depth. A special clearance would be required for multifamily housing, public housing, college housing, mobile homes or Section 8 Housing Assistance Payments of 200-499 units, 200 to 499-bed hospitals or nursing homes, or 100-499 unit subdivisions with lot sizes of greater than 6000 square feet, 200-499 unit subdivisions with lot sizes of less than 6000 square feet, or other projects in excess of $5,000,000 requested mortgage amount.

Finally an environmental impact statement clearance is the complete and fully comprehensive environmental evaluation. An EIS clearance is required for multifamily housing, public housing, college housing, mobile home, Section 8 Housing Assistance Payments, hospitals or nursing homes with 500 beds or more, or any project which is determined to have a significant impact on the quality of the human environment. Obviously size is just one criteria. Although these "thresholds" are automatic triggers, any project irrespective of threshold limits may require a more intensive environmental review depending on the findings during the environmental assessment. HUD, for instance, recognizes "potential controversy" or "related individual factors" as contributory elements which might contribute to a decision to undertake a more comprehensive environmental clearance procedure.

Even though HUD's general policy on environmental considerations applies to all HUD actions, the procedural requirements for environmental clearances shall not apply to those HUD actions which have been determined *not* to be "major federal actions significantly affecting the quality of the human environment." These include an individual action on a one-to-four family dwelling, training grants, or rehabilitation and modernization projects which do not extend the life of a structure twenty (20) years or more. (Exemption from environmental clearances does not exempt these activities from the requirements of Section 106 of the National Historic Preservation Act of 1966 when a property is listed on or nominated to the National Register of Historic Places; planning assistance projects [701 Comprehensive Planning Assistance] are exempted from the procedural requirements but must file an environmental assessment in lieu thereof; with respect to disaster relief activities, actions which provide temporary housing need not abide by environmental clearance procedures, but permanent housing must abide.)

Normal, special, and EIS environmental clearances may be best explained by using the procedures and documents required of insured projects, subdivisions and low rent housing projects. These are the most common undertakings for the bulk of users of this handbook. Although an abbreviated procedure—it is perhaps the clearest. The person conducting the clearance employs "Instructions for Completing the Normal and a Special Environmental Clearance Form for Housing Projects," the prelude to Appendix C-5 to Department Guide 1390.1, as a guide. (See Addendum B-2).

This instruction sheet lists four ratings which are applied to component environmental factors associated with the project. (These are the elements of the thumbnail sketch discussed previously and appears as Appendix B.) A rating of "A" indicates the component is acceptable (no special problems associated with this item—adverse impacts are negligible); "B" indicates the component is questionable (problems associated with the items call for discretion in granting environmental approval—ameliorative measures should be pursued); "C" indicates the component as undesirable or unacceptable (problems associated with these items are serious and rejection may be mandated by specific environmental or program policies—ameliorative measures should be vigorously pursued; approval is allowed only when justified by a careful examination and comparison of alternatives); "NA" indicates an environmental factor is not applicable to the project.

For normal environmental clearance, if there are no marginal ("B") or unacceptable ("C") ratings on any item, the person conducting the analysis recommends the acceptability of the proposal on environmental grounds. Where a marginal rating is assigned to any item a memorandum as to the findings on that item must accompany the report. Marginal ratings for serious problems are cause for rejection. Where an unacceptable rating is assigned to any item the person completing the analysis consults and obtains concurrence of the Environmental Clearance Officer concerning further disposition of the proposed action (i.e., rejection, modification, further study, the preparation of a special clearance, or the preparation of an EIS).

For special environmental clearance with no marginal or unacceptable ratings, the procedure is basically the same as the normal clearance. Where a marginal rating exists on any item of a serious nature, an EIS is frequently required. Where an unacceptable rating exists, further disposition of the project must be checked with the ECO as in the case for normal environmental clearance.

For EIS clearance, a full impact statement is prepared following the format of ECO-1 and the guidelines of this handbook.

Required Forms and Documents

The basic "how to" manual for HUD's EIS is Departmental Handbook 1390.1 which was published July 18, 1973 (Docket No. N-73-182 38-FR 19182) revised February 22, 1974 and November 4, 1974.

The manual contains procedures and policies to be employed in carrying out EIS's. Its appendices consist of the following:

APPENDIX A-1	Project Level Actions Subject to Threshold Criteria
APPENDIX A-2	Other HUD Actions With Special Requirements
APPENDIX B-1	Initial Level of Environmental Clearance
APPENDIX C-1	Form ECO-1 (Applicant's EIS Information)
APPENDIX C-2	Form ECO-2 (Normal Environmental Clearance)
APPENDIX C-3	Form ECO-3 (Special Environmental Clearance)
APPENDIX C-4	Environmental Finding Resulting from Special Clearance
APPENDIX C-5	Form ECO-2/3 HPMC (Normal and Special Environmental Clearance for Subdivision and Multifamily Projects)

Environmental clearance forms are used by HUD to conduct the required environmental clearance. These are completed by the Area/Insuring Office Technical Staff and concurred in by the Area Planning Office Technical Staff.

For project level actions other than HUD insured projects, subdivisions, and low rent housing projects, a form ECO-1 (Environmental Clearance Officer) is used to solicit information from the applicant. This form lists the basic areas to be covered in an EIS and is identical to the guidelines (in their unembellished form) that appear in a subsequent section of this handbook.

An independent environmental assessment and evaluation is conducted by HUD on form ECO-2 for actions requiring normal clearance, on form ECO-3 for actions requiring special clearance, and a full blown EIS following the format of ECO-1 for those actions which require an EIS. Whether or not this exact procedure is continued, HUD clearly states that the burden for assessing environmental impact at the federal level rests with HUD and not the developer/applicant.

For HUD insured projects, subdivisions and low rent housing projects no environmental information (Form ECO-1) is initially required of the applicant additionally, an abbreviated environmental clearance form ECO-2/3 HPMC (Housing Production and Mortgage Credit) replaces the Normal (ECO-2) and Special (ECO-3) Environmental Clearance forms. This special set of requirements was designed to expedite processing of these types of project level actions.

HUD PROCEDURE PASSED TO THE LOCAL LEVEL

Previously there has been pointed out a distinction made by HUD as to the federal EIS *processing* of insured projects, subdivisions, and low rent housing projects and all other HUD actions for which environmental assessments must be made. There is also another distinction made by HUD as to program: those HUD actions which will be evaluated at the federal level and those which will be evaluated at the local level. Most actions will now be evaluated at the local level.

Section 104(h) of Title I of the Housing and Community Development Act of 1974 (Pub. L. 93-383, 42 USC 5301 et seq.) authorizes a procedure under which local communities with approved community development applications assume for specific projects the review procedures and decision-making responsibilities previously discussed as applying at the federal level to the Secretary of the Department of Housing and Urban Development.

What is being said here is that for those Title I projects which HUD grants funding under the Community Development Act, the EIS responsibility will be borne by the local chief ececutive; in most cases the mayor. He then assumes NEPA responsibility for federally sanctioned actions within his political jurisdiction. If, in fact, the mayor fails to adhere to his NEPA responsibility, he may be sued in place of the HUD Secretary.

Basically most of the policy and procedures which HUD personnel use to evaluate non-Title I actions at the federal level have been passed down to the mayor and his staff to carry out the appropriate evaluations locally. Except for the first, a mandatory documentation of the EIS process at the local level, even the forms are similar. Appendix I to "Environmental Review Procedures: Proposed Policies and Procedures," published October 10, 1974 (Docket No. 4-74-297-39 FR 19858), is the format for the required Environmental Review Record which documents the local clearance process. Appendix II is HUD Handbook 1390.1 to guide completion of the EIS and ECO-1, *if necessary*, to solicit the required information to be contained in the EIS. Appendix III contains the combined form ECO-2/3 for evaluating the thumbnail sketch clearance for HUD insured projects, subdivisions, and low rent housing projects. Appendix IV is a cover sheet used in processing the project's evaluation.

The regulations implementing Title I consist of slightly revised definitions, policies to guide the mayor assuming NEPA responsibilities, and an extensive environmental review procedure to channel the processing of environmental assessments. It further indicates that preliminary Title I funds are available from HUD to assist the mayor in carrying out his NEPA responsibilities within the up-to-10-percent preapplication assistance available to all Title I applicants. All non-exempt projects (those other than relocation activities, comprehensive planning activities, developing a policy-management-planning capacity, continuation of Model Cities/Urban Renewal programs, upgrading public services, etc.) included in the community development program of an applicant (municipality) are required to be subjected to environmental review by the applicant. As in the case of federal evaluation through the environmental review process, the municipality must arrive at a determination of whether or not any proposed project will result in any environmental impact: the nature, magnitude, and extent of any such impact, whether or not any changes can be made to eliminate or minimize adverse impacts, and the level of environmental clearance which is appropriate.

Regulations enforcing Title I list two levels of environmental clearance offered based upon the environmental finding of the municipality:

(a) finding that request for a release of funds for projects is not a major federal action significantly affecting the quality of the human environment. (EIS not required.)

(b) finding that request for a release of funds for projects is a major federal action significantly affecting the quality of the human environment. (EIS is required.)

The environmental finding repeats the process discussed earlier. Essentially one carries out the process of (a) determining existing conditions, (b) identifying environmental impacts, and (c) examining identified impacts (internal and external modifications and alternatives). This is nothing more than the procedure discussed previously for the combining of Normal/Special Clearance procedure for HUD insured projects, subdivisions, and low rent housing projects. If the project passes through the combined clearance procedure with no marginal or unacceptable ratings, the project is deemed *not* to be a major federal action significantly affecting the quality of the human environment. If in either case marginal elements appear which are of a serious nature or if the project:

(a) results in a 50 percent change in the density, vehicular traffic, demand for energy, or demand for other public services in the area environmentally affected by the project,

(b) is a neighborhood facilities project having site acreage of 50,000 square feet, or gross floor area of 30,000 square feet,

(c) is an open space land project involving (1) sanitary landfill; (2) impoundment of two surface acres or twenty-five acre feet of water; (3) 50 acres, or more; and (4) conversions of open space land to non-open space land uses,

(d) is a neighborhood development project conversion from conventional urban renewal to neighborhood development; is a change in NDP area of plans,

(e) is an above ground reservoir and standpipe; is a source development project including major river impoundments, raw water reservoirs, well fields, treatment plants, treated water transmission or sewage collection lines which pass through, are adjacent to, or serve undeveloped areas of 50 acres or more.

the project may or may not be a major federal action significantly affecting the quality of the human environment, yet an EIS should be seriously considered.

Finally, if marginal elements appear or the project:

(a) involves maximum sound signal or substance emitting levels which exceed those established by law or competent regulation,

(b) has an adverse impact (which cannot be satisfactorily removed or mitigated) upon any historic property,

(c) involves any violation which cannot be satisfactorily removed or mitigated, or criteria or standards under applicable laws or regulations governing environmental considerations such as: the Clean Air Act; the Federal Water Pollution Control Act; HUD Noise Regulation (1390.2); the Coastal Zone Management Act; the Fish and Wildlife Coordination Act; the National Flood Insurance Act; and similar federal and state laws and regulations,

(d) involves the removal, demolition, conversion or emplacement of a total of 500 or more dwelling units,

(e) passes through or is adjacent to water or sewer facilities or serves underdeveloped areas of 100 acres or more,

the project will be definitely deemed to be a major federal action significantly affecting the quality of the human environment.

Once the clearance is issued HUD mandates provisions for publication and dissemination of the EIS and promulgates factors to consider in the scheduling of public hearings. These are basically the same as the procedures outlined earlier in the sections of the Pre-EIS Review Process and the Environmental Review Record.

THE OVERLAPPING REQUIREMENTS OF A-95 REVIEW

The second review process required for both federal and local public EIS for filings (A-95 Review) predates NEPA. This is the advisory role delegated to areawide planning organizations by the Office of Management and Budget in accordance with the Intergovernmental Cooperation Act of 1968. The procedure is detailed in OMB Circular A-95, which has undergone several revisions since it was originally issued in July 1969. The circular requires that anyone applying for assistance under federal programs ranging from Urban Rat Control to Airport and Airways Development must first submit a notice of intent to the appropriate areawide agency and to the state's clearinghouse for federal applications. Most of the areawide agencies are Councils of Government (COG's), voluntary associations of local jurisdictions engaged in a variety of planning activities at the regional level.

Virtually all of the federal programs providing financing, mortgage assistance or mortgage insurance for new housing are covered by A-95. In the case of housing, unlike other programs, the applicant developer need not contact the areawide agency directly. After receiving and assigning a file number to an application for feasibility analysis (ASP 1 or 2013), the FHA office forwards it to the areawide and state clearinghouses. The clearinghouses, in turn, advise affected and interested local governments and state, regional, and local agencies of the application.

The type of review conducted at the regional level varies depending upon the size and complexity of the region and the size and interests of the regional agency and its staff. But even if the areawide organization has nothing to say about the project's relationship to its own plans and policies, it may pass on to the FHA comments received from its member jurisdictions or other agencies.

From the developer/applicant's standpoint there are a number of functions the areawide agency can provide to facilitate processing at both the federal and local levels. The clearinghouse can operate as a communication link between the local agency and the FHA or other affected agencies. Early contact can eliminate the possibility of unanticipated conflict arising after sizable investments of time and money have been made. Early contact between the two levels of government with responsibility for project approval may also minimize unnecessary duplication in their review activities and even reduce the scope of the EIS that must be filed. HUD's environmental procedures require that a copy of the ECO-1 when required be submitted to the areawide agency. In addition to reviewing this material themselves, some clearinghouses pass it on to local agencies for their input. Finally, the clearinghouse can also be a good source of information about the potential concerns of affected local and regional agencies, plans for competing or conflicting projects, the availability of necessary services, and conflicts likely to arise.

CONCLUSION

While indeed these processes appear confusing, the basic point to remember is that if you have an option in adopting an environmental assessment process locally, gear the private EIS filing to extant public requirements. This is what has been done here. This procedure offers the dual advantage of giving the developer the greatest amount of flexibility in terms of his reaction to potential EIS processing and additionally avoiding duplication of any previous effort that has been undertaken.

Once this is done remember that there is a two-step process to EIS—an initial determinance of significance and a subsequent filing or non-filing of the EIS. Keep a record of what takes place locally and be cognizant of both the public's and other upper echelons of government's desire to participate in any review process.

ADDENDUM A-1—Proposed HUD Actions Which Require Special Environmental Clearance or Environmental Impact Statement Clearance
(Note: For programs not listed, consult the Assistant Secretary for Community Planning and Development)

Program	Decision points	Thresholds
Housing Assistance or Insurance:[1] New Construction or substantial rehabilitation of[2]		
—one-to-four family structures.........	Issuance of feasibility letter or major change in letter or project (ASP-6).	100 lot subdivision where typical lot size is 6000 sq. ft. or greater; 200 lot subdivision where typical lot size is under 6000 sq. ft.
—multifamily structures	Issuance of SAMA letter or major change in letter or project. Reservation of contract authority to State and local agencies for interest reduction assistance and rent supplement payments for uninsured projects.[3]	200-unit multifamily project (including scattered sites), or requested mortgage amount exceeds $5,000,000.
—public housing	Letter of notification of tentative site approval or approval of major change.	200-unit public housing project (including scattered sites).
—college housing	Approval of fund reservation for college housing or major amendatory.	200-student project.
—mobile homes	Issuance of SAMA letter or major change in letter or project.	200-unit mobile home park.
—nursing homes	Issuance of SAMA letter or major change in letter or project.	200-bed nursing home.
—hospitals[4]	Issuance of SAMA letter or major change in letter or project.	200-bed hospital.
—group practice facilities	Issuance of SAMA letter or major change in letter or project. Notification of selection of preliminary proposals.	Facilities with site acreage of 30,000 sq. ft., or gross floor area of 30,000 sq. ft. 200-unit project.
—Section 8 Housing Assistance Payments Program.		
Substantial rehabilitation or property, disposition of: 1-to-4 family structures. Multifamily structures. College housing. Mobile homes. Nursing homes. Hospitals. Group practice. Facilities.	1. For rehabilitation, feasibility determination. 2. For Project Rehab, submission of proposal to central office. 3. For property disposition, approval of disposition program.	50 contiguous or noncontiguous 1-to-4 -family structures/lots. 100-unit multifamily project (including scattered sites). 200-student project—college housing. 100-unit mobile home park. 100-bed nursing home.

ADDENDUM A-1 (Continued)

Program	Decision points	Thresholds
Model Cities (planned variations)	1. All action years or major amendments, to the extent that the activities have not been previously evaluated. 2. Approval of application for individual project within Model Cities program.[5]	100-bed hospital. Group practice facility with site acreage of 50,000 ft.[6] or gross floor area of 30,000 ft.[6] Approval memorandum or letter of approval, whichever is sooner.
Neighborhood facilities	Approval of allocation order or approval subject to validation of funds (whichever is sooner), or approval of major amendatory.	See appropriate categorical program Site acreage of 50,000 ft.[6], or gross floor area of 30,000 ft.[6]
Open space land	Approval of allocation order or approval subject to validation of funds (whichever is sooner), or approval of major amendatory. Approval for conversion.	1. All sanitary landfill projects. 2. Impoundment of 2 surface acres or 25 acre-feet of water. 3. 50 acres. 4. All conversions of open space land acquired with HUD assistance to non-open space uses not originally approved by HUD. *See* Water and sewer.
Public facility loans[7]	Approval of allocation order or approval subject to validation of funds (whichever is sooner), or approval of major amendatory.	All urban renewal projects.
Urban renewal:[8] Conventional	Approval of part I or approval of major amendatory.	
Neighborhood development program[7]	Approval of allocation order or approval subject to validation of funds, whichever is sooner.	1. All first year NDP's and conversions from conventional urban renewal to NDP. 2. Subsequent action years. To the extent that the urban renewal plan has not been previously evaluated and/or changes in area or plans.
Water and sewer	Approval of application or major amendatory.	1. All above ground reservoirs and stand pipes. 2. All source development projects, including major river impoundments, raw water reservoirs, well fields, and treatment plants.

ADDENDUM A-1 (Continued)

Program	Decision points	Thresholds
Flood and disaster insurance program.....	Issuance of special flood plain or mudslide area delineations. Community eligibility.	3. Treated water transmission or sewage collection lines which pass through, are adjacent to, or serve undeveloped areas of 50 acres or more. 1. Variance from normal practice defined by FIA. 2. Variance of land use and control measures from established FIA criteria.

1. Project selection criteria are not a substitute for environmental clearance.
2. Phase three Breakthrough housing projects are subject to environmental clearance procedures in the same way as other housing projects.
3. This handbook shall also apply to HUD approval of interest subsidy on existing properties. However, the environmental assessment does not have to address the impact of the construction of the project on the environment since it has already taken place. All other environmental factors must be assessed.
4. HEW has the lead role in environmental evaluation and clearance of proposed hospitals. HUD has responsibility for clearance and conformance with Departmental policies and standards to the extent that such clearance is not conducted by HEW.
5. For projects using supplementary funds which result in the construction or acquisition of capital facilities not included in HUD categorical programs, the appropriate environmental clearance shall be prepared prior to the award of the supplemental grant.
6. Project selection criteria are not a substitute for environmental clearance.
7. Project selection systems are not a substitute for environmental clearance.
8. For projects in the National Capital area, refer to agreement between HUD and the National Capital Planning Commission.

Source: Department of Housing and Urban Development, "Protection and Enhancement of Environmental Quality," *Federal Register* Vol. 39, No. 37, February 22, 1974, pp. 6823-4, as amended.

ADDENDUM A-2—Other HUD Actions with Special Requirements
(Note: Where special requirements are imposed in accordance with this appendix, thresholds set forth in Addendum A-1 do not apply.)

Action	Decision Point	Requirement
New construction or substantial rehabilitation of residential or other noise sensitive land uses such as nursing homes, hospitals, group practice facilities, in unacceptable noise zone (circular 1390.2).	Decision point stated in addendum A-1.	Environmental impact statement.
New construction or substantial rehabilitation of residential or other noise sensitive land uses such as nursing homes, hospitals, group practice facilities, in discretionary (normally unacceptable) noise zone (circular 1390.2), which is new development in a largely undeveloped area.	do	Do.
New construction or substantial rehabilitation of residential or other noise sensitive land uses in discretionary (normally unacceptable) noise zone (circular 1390.2), which is infill in existing development.	do	Special environmental clearance.
New Communities: Debt guarantee or certification of eligibility or interest loan.	Authorization by Community Development Corporation Board of offer of commitment or major change to approved plan.	Environmental impact statement.
New communities: Special planning assistance loan or grant.	Authorization by Community Development Corporation Board of loan or grant.	Environmental assessment as part of planning product.
Multifamily projects of 500 units or more and subdivisions of 500 units or more	Issuance of feasibility letter or major change in letter or project.	Environmental impact statement.
Any project which has an effect on a property listed on, or nominated to, the National Register of Historic Places.	Decision point stated in addendum A-1.	Special environmental clearance.
Any project which has an adverse effect on a property listed on, or nominated to, the National Register of Historic Places.	Decision point stated in addendum A-1.	Environmental impact statement. Request review by Advisory Council on Historic Preservation.

ADDENDUM A-2 (Continued)

Action	Decision Point	Requirement
Legislation	Departmental decision to sponsor legislation.	Finding of inapplicability or draft and final environmental impact statement.
Regulations which have potential for significantly affecting the quality of the human environment.	Publication in *Federal Register* of notice of proposed rule making.	Finding of inapplicability or draft environmental impact statement.
	Promulgation	Final environmental impact statement, where applicable.
Policy and guidance documents which have potential for significantly affecting the quality of the human environment	A-85 clearance	Finding of inapplicability or draft environmental impact statement.
	Promulgation	Final environmental impact statement, where applicable.

1. Project actions affected by Circular 1390.2 require that projects located in the Unacceptable or Discretionary-Normally Unacceptable noise exposure zone require special approvals and must incorporate noise attenuation measures.

Note: It is recognized that in high density areas, size alone need not necessarily imply a significant impact on the quality of the human environment. Therefore, special exemption to this threshold may be granted by the Assistant Secretary for CPD where typical densities in the immediate environs of the proposed multifamily project exceeds 50 units per acre (LUI of 5.2 to 7.3). Area wide waivers may be granted for large dense urban areas or sections thereof having such densities and meeting criteria established by the Assistant Secretary. Delegations of authority to approve such waivers may be granted to the Regional Offices at the discretion of the Assistant Secretary.

Source: Department of Housing and Urban Development, "Procedures for Protection and Enhancement of Environmental Quality," *Federal Register*, Vol. 39, No. 213, November 4, 1974, p. 38923.

ADDENDUM B-1
INSTRUCTIONS FOR COMPLETING THE NORMAL AND
SPECIAL ENVIRONMENTAL CLEARANCE FORM FOR
HOUSING PROJECTS
(Note: A facsimile of the actual form follows in Addendum B-2.)

I. *GENERAL INSTRUCTIONS*

This form combines HUD's Normal and Special Environmental Clearances and provides for a detailed and systematic assessment of a potential housing site and its environment. It covers both environmental and marketability issues. The following describes in brief the procedures to be followed in completing the form.

RATING

Based on the best available information, supplemented as necessary, each environmental component is to be rated as follows:

A *The component is acceptable.* There are no special problems associated with this item. Adverse impacts are negligible; other effects are neutral or beneficial.

B *The component is questionable.* Problems associated with item call for discretion in granting environmental approval to the project. Ameliorative measures should be pursued and may be mandated by specific environmental or program policies.

C *The component is undesirable or unacceptable.* Problems associated with this item are serious and rejection may be mandated by specific environmental or program policies. Ameliorative measures should be vigorously pursued. Approval is allowed only when justified by a careful examination and comparison of alternatives.

NA *The environmental factor is not applicable to this project.* For example access to local schools is not applicable to elderly housing projects; coastal zone environmental policies do not apply to inland projects, etc.

SOURCE/DOCUMENTATION

The Environmental Clearance Form, plus the supporting evidence constitute the complete Environment Clearance for the project. In the column marked "source/documentation," refer to specific attachments or to specific portions of the project file or "FO" (Field Observation) for observations made during the field inspection which were used as the basis for the indicated rating. Documentation may include studies or portions of studies conducted by others, written explanations and clarification by the reviewer based on field visit, or conversations with experts, or it may include maps, or other information used as the basis for the rating and conclusions on the form. Where material is of a nature that cannot be attached or inserted in the project files, it should be referenced on the form.

ADDENDUM B-1 (Continued)

II. *SPECIFIC INSTRUCTIONS*
(Items correspond to designation on clearance form)

A. PROJECT IDENTIFICATION.
Self-explanatory

B. COMPLIANCE WITH APPLICABLE STANDARDS AND PLANS
1. Self-explanatory
2. Self-explanatory
3. Self-explanatory
4. The following environmental policies and regulations are applicable

Historic Properties

— National Historic Preservation Act of 1966 (PL 89-665); esp. Sec. 106

— Preservation of Historic and Archaeological Data Act of 1974 (PL 93-291)

— EO 11593, Protection and Enhancement of the Cultural Environment 1971

— Procedures for Protection and Historic and Cultural Properties, Advisory Council on Historic Preservation, 36 CFR 800.

Noise

— HUD Handbook 1390.2, Noise Abatement and Control, Departmental Policy, Responsibilities and Standards, 1971.

Flood Plain

— Flood Disaster Protection Act of 1973 (PL 93-234), and implementing regulations.

— Title 24, Chapter X, Subchapter B, National Flood Insurance Program

Coastal Zones and Wetlands

— Coastal Zone Management Act of 1972 (PL 92-583). Also, any applicable State legislation or regulations

Air Quality

— Clean Air Act and Clean Air Act Amendments of 1970 USEPA Implementing Regulations, especially

— National, Primary and Secondary Ambient Air Quality Standard 1971

— Review of Indirect Sources, 1974

— Applicable State legislation or regulations

ADDENDUM B-1 (Continued)

C. SITE SUITABILITY ANALYSIS

This section is designed to determine if the site and surrounding area represents a suitable living environment for project residents, including whether it is adequately served by community services and utilities. Issues concern the impact of the environment on the project.

Under "Facilities and Services" (Items 11-19), a separate rating is required for (1) access to the facility or service, and (2) adequacy of the facility or service.

In order to clarify the meaning of terms used on the form, the following is a listing of representative issues. They are presented in the form of questions to simplify discussion.

1. *Slope Stability*

   Will the project be subject to hazardous landslides, falling rock, or other unstable slope conditions due to site topographic or geologic conditions?

2. *Foundation Conditions*

   Can excessive deformations of foundations occur because of changes in moisture content, soil swelling or shrinkage, frost action on soils, liquification, substantial soil loss from construction practices, water or wind erosion, inadequate weight bearing capacity, or subsidence due to sink hole, mine excavation or water withdrawal?

3. *Terrain*

   Is the site subject to unusual terrain features such as steep slopes, abutting rock formations, or other conditions affecting construction, drainage, or livability. Does the proposed development appear to take advantage of the natural features of the site and area?

4. *Soil Permeability*

   Will impermeable layers such as clay affect construction, drainage, or water infiltration required to replenish groundwater supplies? Will impermeable layers result in groundwater contamination due to septic tank or well development?

5. *Groundwater*

   Is the site subject to rapid water withdrawal problems which change the depth or character of the water table, affect water supply, septic tank use or vegetation?

6. *Natural Hazards*

   Are there unusual risks from natural hazards such as geologic fault, flash floods, volcanic activity, mudslides or fires, or from the presence of ponds, or hazardous terrain features?

ADDENDUM B-1 (Continued)

7. *Man-made Hazards*

Are there unwarranted risks from man-made hazards such as inadequate separation of pedestrian and vehicular traffic, roadway design or lack of traffic control, visual obstructions, improper use of materials, or presence of hazardous materials such as uranium mill tailings, or liquid petroleum storage areas, or the presence of potentially hazardous industrial activity or material in the surrounding area?

8. *Nuisances*

Is the site subject to nuisances from odors, vibrations, unsightly areas, nearby landfills, inconveniences or other nuisances?

9. *Compatibility in Use and Scale with the Surrounding Area*

Is the project compatible with the surrounding area in terms of land use density, scale, mass, texture and architectural design?

10. *Neighborhood Character*

Is the project location in an area of physical deterioration, or physical investment? Is it in an area of transition in terms of density or types of land use? Is the development taking place or anticipated in the area compatible with the project?

11. *Elementary Schools*

Does the project location provide for adequate and safe access to school for elementary school age children?

12. *Junior and High Schools*

Does the project location provide adequate and safe access to school for junior and high school age children?

13. *Employment*

Is there adequate access to employment opportunities for proposed occupants? Is there an adequate supply of employment opportunities considering the skill and income requirement of proposed occupants?

14. *Shopping*

Is there adequate and convenient access to shopping?

Are the retail services available to the project adequate to meet the needs of proposed occupants?

ADDENDUM B-1 (Continued)

15. *Park, Playground and Open Space*

Is there adequate and convenient access to parks, playgrounds and functional open space areas?

Are the park, playgrounds and open space facilities in the project and surrounding area adequate to meet the needs of proposed occupants?

16. *Police and Fire*

Does the project location allow for adequate access for police and fire protection services?

Are the police and fire protection services available to the project adequate to meet the project needs?

17. *Health Care and Social Services*

Is there adequate access to hospitals, emergency facilities, clinics and doctor services?

Are the medical services adequate to meet the needs of the residents?

Does the location provide convenient access to social services offered by the community such as day care, youth services and special assistance to the aged if required by the proposed occupants?

Are the social services offered adequate to meet special needs of the residents?

18. *Transportation*

Do proposed occupants have convenient access to community transportation services?

Are the transportation services serving the project adequate to meet the project needs in terms of destinations, schedules and transfer requirements?

Are roads adequate for private transportation?

19. *Other Services*

Identify and rate other services not listed above (e.g. cultural) which may be applicable for the proposed occupants.

20-25. *Utilities*

Will the utilities listed adequately serve the proposed occupants?

D. See para. 8-3, HUD Handbook 4010.1.

ADDENDUM B-1 (Continued)

E. IMPACT ON THE ENVIRONMENT

This section is designed for determining how the project will impact on the environment of the site and surrounding area and on the delivery of services elsewhere in the community.

1. *Impact on Unique Geological Features or Resources*

Will project location, construction or activities of project residents adversely impact unique geologic features on or near the site?

2. *Impact on Rock and Soil Stability*

Will the project have an adverse impact on rock and soil stability due to weight of buildings on surficial materials, liquifaction or water infiltration into surrounding soils from man-made impoundments, or transport route construction?

3. *Impact on Soil Erodability*

Will the project make the area substantially more susceptible to erosion because of grading, inadequate vegetative cover during or after construction, inadequate drainage plan or other causes?

4. *Impact on Groundwater (level, flow and quality)*

Will the project impede natural drainage patterns, which cannot be corrected, cause alterations in stream channel form, or otherwise affect groundwater movement? Will construction over recharge areas substantially affect aquifer yields or water quality?

Will erosion or increased weathering rate of bedrock result in groundwater contamination?

5. *Impact on Open Streams and Lakes*

Will erosion, increased runoff, or wastes from the project contaminate open streams and lakes? Will disruptions of water flow affect the characteristics of open streams and lakes?

6. *Impact on Plant and Animal Life*

Are there unique species of plant or animal life particularly susceptible to adverse impact from construction and human habitation?

Is there vegetation present, the loss of which would deny habitat to unique wildlife species, or to a substantial number of different animals? Will such vegetation be preserved?

Will plant or animal life be adversely affected by disruptions to the nutrient cycle or hydrologic balance?

ADDENDUM B-1 (Continued)

7. *Impact on Energy Resources*

Are community energy supplies adequate to accommodate the energy consumption in the project? Are there indications that the project will promote inefficient energy utilization?

8. *Impact on the Social Fabric and Community Structures*

Will the project substantially change the income, racial, ethnic or age distribution of the neighborhood or community?

9. *Displacement of Individuals or Families*

Will the project displace individuals or families?

Will the project destroy or relocate existing jobs, community facilities or small business enterprises?

Is there an adequate relocation plan?

10. *Impact on Aesthetics and Urban Design*

Will the project adversely affect the aesthetic image of the surrounding area? Will the project block views? Is the proposed design integrated with the area in which it is located?

11. *Impact on Existing or Planned Community Facilities*

Is the capacity of the listed community facilities (11-19) adequate to accommodate the higher utilization resulting from the project? Will the availability or quality of the service from the facilities suffer as a result of project usage? Will the project push the facility's utilization rate close to capacity?

F. The reviewer is to give a summary evaluation of the project impact on the issues contained in D in order to determine if further analysis is necessary. This allows the reviewer to record unusual cases in which a project below Special Clearance size thresholds has notable impacts on the environment despite its small size. Also in this section consider changes in site design.

G. In this section the reviewer should determine how the environmental impact of a project interacts with other planned or anticipated development. The reviewer must then indicate the strategy established for incorporating cumulative impacts of developments in that area into this and other project level decisions.

H. *LOCATION AND MARKET* (See HUD Handbooks 4150.1 and 4465.1)

I. *ENVIRONMENTAL FINDINGS*

Findings relate to the disposition of the project and the level of environmental clearance required. The comment section should contain further justification of the

ADDENDUM B-1 (Continued)

finding which is not self evident in previous sections of the form (e.g. analysis and comparison of alternative to a proposed project which involves an unacceptable rating on some component), or other clarifying remarks.

J. *REVIEW AND COMMENT OF ENVIRONMENTAL CLEARANCE OFFICER*

Comments of the Environmental Clearance Officer must cover four items: (1) completeness of the review, (2) adequacy of supporting documentation, (3) assigned ratings and (4) the finding. The ECO is also required to make recommendations on each of the four items.

K. *INSTRUCTIONS BY CHIEF UNDERWRITER*

Self-explanatory.

Source: HUD Transmittal No. 4, 4010.1 CHG, Nov. 1974, Appendix A.

ADDENDUM B-2
NORMAL AND SPECIAL ENVIRONMENTAL CLEARANCE FORM
FOR SUBDIVISION AND MULTIFAMILY PROJECTS

A. PROJECT IDENTIFICATION:

Applicant's Name: _____ Street Address: _____

City or County: _____ State: _____ Zip Code: _____

Phone: _____ Project Name: _____ FHA File No. _____

Project/Subdivision Location: _____

Number of Lots or Units Proposed: _____ Size of Tract (acres/sq. ft.): _____

Demand for housing in this area: Adequate ☐ Reject ☐ If reject, go to Section 1.

For Subdivision Only:

    Has work started? Yes ☐ No ☐ If work has started: Grading is___ % Completed:

    Street improvements are___% Completed. Number of homes under construction:

    Number of homes completed: _____

ENVIRONMENTAL ANALYSIS

Evaluate project and assign a rating: A, B, C. or NA. (See Instructions.)

B. COMPLIANCE WITH STANDARDS:

1. Have A-95 review requirements been met? Yes ☐ No ☐ In process _____

2. Is the project in compliance with the local and regional comprehensive plans? Yes ☐ No ☐

3. Is the project in compliance with local zoning ordinances? Yes ☐ No ☐

4. Compliance with applicable standards:

	Rating	Source/ Documentation		Rating	Source/ Documentation
a. Historic Properties	_____	_____	e. Wetlands	_____	_____
b. Noise	_____	_____	f. Air Quality	_____	_____
c. Flood Plain	_____	_____	g. Other (specify)	_____	_____
d. Coastal Zone	_____	_____		_____	_____

Is the project in violation of applicable standards? Yes ☐ No ☐

Should the project be rejected? Yes ☐ No ☐ If reject, go to Section I. If not, continue the environmental assessment (Section C).

C. SITE SUITABILITY ANALYSIS:

	Rating	Source/ Documentation		Rating	Source/ Documentation
1. Slope stability	_____	_____	6. Natural hazards	_____	_____
2. Foundation conditions.	_____	_____	7. Man-made hazards	_____	_____
3. Terrain	_____	_____	8. Nuisances	_____	_____
4. Soil permeability	_____	_____	9. Compatibility in use and scale with environment	_____	_____
5. Ground water	_____	_____	10. Neighborhood character	_____	_____

ADDENDUM B-2 (Continued)

Services and Facilities	Rating (Access)	Rating (Adequacy)	Source/ Documentation
11. Elementary School	_____	_____	_____
12. Junior and senior high school	_____	_____	_____
13. Employment	_____	_____	_____
14. Shopping	_____	_____	_____
15. Park, playground and open space	_____	_____	_____
16. Police and fire	_____	_____	_____
17. Health care/ social services	_____	_____	_____
18. Transportation	_____	_____	_____
19. Other services:	_____	_____	_____

Utilities	Rating	Source/ Documen- tation		Rating	Source/ Documen- tation
20. Water supply system	____	_____	23. Solid waste disposal	____	_____
21. Sanitary sewer system	____	_____	24. Other utilities	____	_____
22. Storm sewer system	____	_____	25. Paved access to site	____	_____

D. Does project size exceed special clearance size thresholds? Yes □ No □ If yes, continue review (Section E). If not, go to Section F. (See Chapter 8, Handbook 4010.1)

E. IMPACTS ON THE ENVIRONMENT (SPECIAL CLEARANCE):

	Rating	Source/ Documentation
1. Impact on unique geological features or resources	_____	_____
2. Impact on rock and soil stability	_____	_____
3. Impact on soil erodability	_____	_____
4. Impact on ground water (level, flow and quality)	_____	_____
5. Impact on open streams and lakes	_____	_____
6. Impact on plant and animal life	_____	_____
7. Impact on energy resources	_____	_____
8. Impact on social fabric and community structures	_____	_____
9. Displacement of persons or families	_____	_____
10. Impact on aesthetics and urban design	_____	_____
11. Impact on existing or programmed community facilities:	_____	_____

	Rating	Source/ Documen- tation		Rating	Source/ Documen- tation
a. Schools	____	_____	e. Transportation	____	_____
b. Parks, playgrounds & open space	____	_____	f. Water supply system	____	_____
c. Health care and social services	____	_____	g. Sanitary sewer system	____	_____
d. Community services	____	_____	h. Storm sewer system	____	_____
e. Transportation	____	_____	i. Solid waste disposal system	____	_____

ADDENDUM B-2 (Continued)

F. Will the project have notable impacts on the environment? Yes ☐   No ☐ If yes, is further analysis necessary?   Yes ☐   No ☐   Are there alternative site designs that can be considered?   Yes☐   No ☐

COMMENT:

G. Assess the following conditions: (a) Does the project form part of a larger development pattern? Yes ☐ No ☐ : (b) Is the project likely to stimulate additional development? Yes ☐ No ☐ : (c) Are there other developments planned which are or will be impacted by the project? Yes ☐ No ☐

If any of the above area is answered "Yes" indicate how the cumulative environmental impact of the larger development will be addressed. EIS___ Special Environmental Clearance_____701 planning funds_____other_____ . Should this project be delayed until the cumulative impacts are accounted for? Yes ☐ No ☐

COMMENT:

H. LOCATION AND MARKET:

1. Marketability is: Acceptable ☐   Reject ☐   If reject, go to Section I.

2. Most marketable price or rental range is $_____ to $_____ .

3. Most marketable units   0-2 BR_____

                             3 BR _____

                  4 or more _____

4. For Subdivisions:

     Estimated market price of typical lot $_____ to $_____ .

     Typical lot size_____ ft. x _____ ft.

Local Authorities:

1. Local authorities have ☐   have not ☐ approved tentative map.

2. Local officials contacted:

     Name:_____ Title:_____ Phone:_____

     Name:_____ Title:_____ Phone:_____

3. Information obtained and date obtained:

_____

_____

_____

_____

_____

_____

_____

_____

_____

ADDENDUM B-2 (Continued)

I. ENVIRONMENTAL FINDINGS: (Check applicable items)

☐ Reject

☐ EIS Required

☐ No EIS Required. Project is consistent with HUD environmental policies and requirements and is not a major Federal action significantly affecting the quality of the human environment.

☐ Further environmental review is required
Backup material is appended. Yes ☐ No ☐

For Subdivisions Only

☐ Issue Interim Form ASP-5.
Special problems involve:

Sanitary engineering ☐

Site engineering ☐

Site planning ☐

Architecture ☐

☐ Issue ASP-6.
VA has been contacted. Yes ☐ No ☐

COMMENT:

Field Inspection and Assessment made by:_____

Name_____Title_____Date_____

Name_____Title_____Date_____

Name_____Title_____Date_____

J. REVIEW AND COMMENT OF ENVIRONMENTAL CLEARANCE OFFICER:

Environmental Clearance Officer   Date

K. INSTRUCTIONS BY CHIEF UNDERWRITER:

Date

Source: HUD Transmittal No. 4, 4010.1 CHG, Nov. 1974, Appendix B.

INTRODUCTION

No developer should be required to submit an extensive environmental impact statement in a political jurisdiction where environmental planning is nonexistant.

In this section, we hope to provide reasons for the validity of this statement and to discuss the basic questions of EIS responsibility and effectiveness, together with staffing requirements and anticipated costs. Yet, as will become painfully obvious when proceeding through this section, the literature on these subjects is scant.

We ask initially: who should complete the EIS; is the EIS, in its present form, doing the job; and finally, what kinds of personnel are involved in the EIS process and what are their interrelationships?

WHO BEARS THE RESPONSIBILITY OF EIS

One of the most critical areas of environmental impact assessment that has been only briefly addressed is the question of *who* should prepare the impact statement. Should evaluation take place on a project-by-project base with the burden falling on the developer; should it be completed for each project by the municipality?[1]

Additionally, what is the relationship between impact assessment in lands already protected by limited development zoning restrictions and those areas which have no special designation? Finally, as NEPA, little NEPA's on the state level, and mini-NEPA's at the local level bring impact assessment closer and closer to the project itself, what are the interrelationships between these oft-times competing echelons of scrutinizing activities.

Under the federal legislation, EIS is the responsibility of the "lead agency" or arm of government that has direct supervisory control or funding responsibility for the action.

Lead Agency refers to the Federal agency which has primary authority for committing the Federal government to a course of action with significant environmental impact.[2]

Inherent in this assignment of tasks is a recognition that there is a distinct "arms length" involvement of the agencies of federal government in many aspects of environmental quality.

Under little NEPA's for the most part the same concept prevails. For private projects authorized or sanctioned by a state or local agency through the grant of a permit, rather than initiated at the state or federal level, the responsibilities of the governmental agencies are not as clear.

In California, the decision at both state and local levels has been to place the burden for EIS on the agency that would be called upon to approve the project. This decision rested on a "minimization of advocacy" position taken by drafters of the legislation, to insure that the EIS was not done merely to justify the project. The governing agency was given several alternatives to meet *its* responsibilities: First, it could hire a consultant to do the report and then bill the developer for the cost of its preparation. Second, it could do the report itself, but in preparing the report it could compel the developer to provide basic information about the project that would enable the city or the state agency to do the report.

In California the second alternative has been the most prevalent. The developer is asked to provide a "draft EIS,"[3] basically a specification of the intended development and foreseeable impacts. The *public agency* is then required to revise or amend the assessment and submit it as an independent judgment of the development's potential impact.

In the Northeast, particularly New Jersey, this is not the case. The *developer* is required to prepare the EIS at his own cost in accordance with ordinance specifications, and then incur a filing fee which serves to cover both the administrative and evaluative costs of project filing.[4]

Amendments to the Cherry Hill, N.J. Zoning and Subdivision Ordinances exemplify this procedure:

Sect. 1-3   "An Environmental Impact Statement is required in standard site plans where the project involves five (5) acres or more of undeveloped land."

Sect. 3(q)   "The Planning Board or the Environmental Commission may require the opinion of experts in their review of the EIS."

Sect. 4(k)-14 "Fees for the costs of such consultation described in paragraph C above shall be paid by the applicant."

To the purist, this latter situation would seem to be an intolerable one. The basic impartiality of the EIS document has been thwarted or, at best, only partially restored through the imposition of a filing fee to keep the developer honest.

The naivety of this position and the accompanying view of government as an impartial agent of the public interest has been exposed in a number of instances by Norman Williams. Williams describes the fourth period in American land use control as one in which there is a sadder and wiser mood about government objectives.

It is recognized that many restrictions on developer's property rights are needed in the modern world, to prevent development which will really harm neighbors or the environment generally. But it is also recognized that local land use restrictions may also serve a non-legitimate purpose, indeed sometimes, no real purpose at all—that is, they may be exclusionary in intent and/or effect, or merely the product of a quite parochial vision, or sometimes unduly harsh with little compensating public benefit—or merely inept.[5]

A local governmental fiefdom may have just as selfish reasons for fixing the outcome of an impact evaluation as the developer himself. If a community has taken a position of "no growth" based upon "desired community size" or "optimum servicing level" environmental concern can indeed be misused.[6] The idea that government does not take its own advocacy position is a thing of the past. Indeed, the planned unit development literature has recognized the bargaining positions of both the private and public sector and has instituted a forum with recommended procedure for it to take place.

INCREMENTAL EIS's OR COMPREHENSIVE ENVIRONMENTAL PLANNING

The question of EIS responsibility skirts the issue of whether or not EIS is indeed doing the job. Is the environment and the total community better off as a result of the EIS process?

Some seasoned experts say *no*. Within the present state of the art, they hold that the environmental impact statement is a simplistic approach to complex issues,[7] relating neither to the regulatory nor the planning processes, incapable of estimating the cumulative impact of multiple actions or the *probability* of an impact on-site or the *possibility* of an impact off-site. They do not distinguish clearly between the identification and evaluation of impacts or specify different levels of alternatives—at the site, in the design, and so forth.[8] The EIS, in their opinion, provides only an incremental perspective rather than a sequential and comprehensive viewpoint.[9]

Professor Donald Hagman notes, and correctly so, that EIS is the antithesis of comprehensive land use control. Under the planning process, the plan is adopted first—if proposals are not in accordance with the plan as expressed through its regulatory ordinances, they are not approved.[10]

Under NEPA and its implementing mechanism, EIS, a proposal is imagined for a particular place and the impacts of that proposal are judged often in the absence of guidelines from the community.[11]

What is advocated by Hagman and many others[12] is a more systematic approach which would achieve an increasing level of specificity in terms of environmental assessment both as the area under scrutiny decreases and as the level of projection proceeds from plan to project.

The proposal to meet the objectives of the environmental impact assessment laws by relating them to planning processes should involve a *phased approach*. Rather than a final product with an accompanying or subsequent assessment, it is recommended that there be a series of increasingly more specific evaluations.

The first step that should be built into the planning process is a requirement for a systematic, overall analysis of the environmental characteristics of an entire jurisdiction. This should be at a general level but be comprehensive in terms of geography and major features of the environment. The closest thing to this approach today is the Natural Resources Inventory.

The second level of planning analysis and planning review would take place at the subcommunity level. Certain areas of the community should be delineated, perhaps in accord with a community growth policy which specifies the areas with the highest priority. Analysis and planning for these subareas should be at a detail sufficient to indicate key constraints of the environmental setting. It is at this level that major alternatives *first* can be carefully identified and evaluated. Thus, most off-site influences which are often documented redundantly by adjacent owners could be evaluated at the same time. Gross impacts on public services, wildlife habitats, and major transportation factors should be considered for areas that are very large and for other impacts going far beyond the limits of any single parcel line or project.[13]

In terms of the actual development review process, the environmental impact report should be merged with zoning and subdivision review into a new policy-based administrative review process. This should be a two-step process similar to the planned unit development process. First, the community should be "staked out" into areas of greater, average, or less than average environmental sensitivity. Then, a developer having a tract of land within any one of these areas would be required to submit an EIS and other analyses as mandated by the filing process. Depending upon community goals in terms of cost revenue, environmental sensitivity, economic growth, or whatever, the application would be given a denial or a tentative initial approval.

Land suitability mapping as exemplified by McHarg in Medford Township, New Jersey,[14] Battelle's Land Use Trade Off Model (LUTOM) being implemented in Beaufort and Jasper Counties, South Carolina,[15] or impact zoning of Rahenkamp, Sachs, and Wells, which is the basis for the regulatory ordinances of Duxbury, Massachusetts,[16] are the type of approaches that bring environmental impact directly within the confines of the planning process yet minimize the burden of impact analysis thrust upon the developer. Most of the previously espoused arguments against the impact statement as the vehicle for environmental review—incrementalism, disjointedness, and lack of relationship to the comprehensive plan—are also minimized through these approaches.

The EIS submission is terse and inexpensive, if the community has already done its homework. If the community has specified what type and how much development will be permitted, all that is necessary in the EIS submission and review is mutual recognition that those general land limitations have been observed. Projects, in effect, are judged in relation to a plan that has already made all the environmental, social, and economic trade offs. The EIS then becomes an on-site inventory and assessment for each project, to be weighed against local and regional inventories. Each application and assessment filed will augment the baseline resource information; this localizing and updating of information becomes a residual benefit of each application.[17] Such a system works to the advantage of the locality and the developers by avoiding the wholesale repetition of environmental analyses as subsequent EIS's are filed.

Unfortunately, this merging of the impact analysis, the comprehensive plan, and regulatory ordinances is proceding at a very slow rate. While NEPA has spread significantly to the local level, little effort has been made to incorporate environmental concerns into the comprehensive plan. The comprehensive plan itself in effect is being subjected to an EIS filing![18] This is an integral part of the California local planning process and is also mandated by the Department of Housing and Urban Development, if a municipality desires to prepare its plan with a grant from the Comprehensive Planning and Management Assistance Program (701).[19] While these comprehensive plan "assessments" are quite general, the requirement seems to us to be misapplied. Environmental sensitivity must derive from the process that formulates goals for community development, not as a result of their impact.[20]

WHAT DO EIS's COST AND
WHO SHOULD BE REQUIRED TO PAY

The price charged by a consultant firm to prepare an EIS can range from several thousand dollars for a standard subdivision to several hundred thousand dollars for a project such as a new community in an undeveloped area, without any public facilities or services. Special soil surveys or traffic analyses required by the local jurisdiction or warranted by unique project characteristics can, of course, also increase the final cost for smaller projects. If the primary responsibility for EIS preparation rests with the agency staff, the fee may be a flat one or can vary depending on the amount of staff time required. The California Environmental Quality Act and other similar state acts purposely left the question of fees open, stating only that public agencies may charge "reasonable" fees to recover their estimated costs both for analysis and subsequent monitoring. The definition of reasonable is, however, clearly open to interpretation. The City of Oakland charges $100 for reviewing a developer's EIS and preparing the final version to be approved by the City Planning Commission. Neighboring San Leandro, however, requires a $25 filing fee for reviewing and processing the applicant's EIS, plus $10 for each page over three—a total of $495 for a 50-page report. An additional fee may be levied by San Leandro to cover the cost of hiring consultants to assist the City in evaluating an applicant's EIS. In Beverly Hills, councilmen deciding whether to hire three new personnel to review EIS's were told that consultants were charging $30 to $50 per hour to prepare EIS's and that even routine reports were costing $2,500.[21] The City of Los Angeles, anticipating a cost of $865,000 in 1973, proposed to charge $30 to $1,000 per application to recoup some of the loss.

While applicants have chafed at the considerable cost of submitting an EIS in line with a local agency's specifications, some planners and many conservation groups have taken issue with requirements which force them to accept an EIS prepared by the applicant or his consultant regardless of level or cost or detail or procedures followed. After all, the argument goes, he who pays the piper calls the tune and you can't expect a project proponent to pay for an extensive evaluation of the negative effects of his own development. Even though the requirements in several states and in recent HUD legislation state that a developer-prepared EIS must be subjected to independent evaluation and analysis, conservation groups note that all too many jurisdictions will shirk that responsibility if no opposition to the project is anticipated.

It would appear that *within reason* the organization or individuals destined to receive profit from the completed project should contribute to the costs of the project's impact assessment. In the PUD literature, fees for impact analysis (typically cost-revenue) are a fairly standard practice—yet frequently this imposition of costs is accompanied by a rezoning which may grant either a higher order use or density increase. EIS, however, is an additional layer of cost which may be grafted on a standard development with no land-use bonus. Those costs will ultimately be passed on by the developer to the housing consumer. EIS's for low rent housing and their attendant costs are obviously a thorny problem.

As noted earlier, local environmental planning may serve to reduce the costs of impact analyses. If at a minimum a Natural Resource Inventory has been performed or better yet, if development overlays are present, both the EIS burden and the resultant cost will be significantly reduced. Nonetheless, EIS *does* incur a cost—this cost, through local ordinances, is being assigned to the developer. Cost frequently varies inversely with local sophistication—this is not a good sign nor should it be perpetuated through local legislation.

THE QUESTION OF PERSONNEL

Once the questions of who bears the responsibilities and costs for environmental impact assessment have been decided, the next question is what type of individuals should be assembled for the analysis. The research group would be wise to draw upon representatives from economics, planning, architecture, engineering, sociology, law, the physical and biological sciences, and public organizations. These specialists and public officials should be brought together for general project reviews in order to expose impacts which lie on the interfaces of their specialties and interests. At a minimum, one physical or biological scientist; one planner, lawyer, or social scientist; and an architect, engineer, or other specialist drawn from the category most relevant to the project should be engaged. One or more public representatives should be invited to participate. In order to achieve a comprehensive and systematic review, it is absolutely critical that the specialists and citizen participants meet early in the study to share thoughts and data about the project and also to exchange views on the appropriate emphasis of the investigation.

The advent of the environmental impact statement has resulted in the creation of a burgeoning and often lucrative industry—environmental consulting. The San Francisco telephone directory's Yellow Pages include almost two columns of Environmental and Ecological Services. Some of them are rejuvenated sanitary engineers, architects and planners; others, newly organized firms with names like Environmental Impact Appraisal Co. and Environmental Impact Planning Corp. Many reputable planning and engineering firms have augmented their staffs to meet the new requirements, and these usually supply the most competent and diverse services. But a host of biologists, sociologists, hydrologists, and others have also set up shop and are available for consultation on specific topics. The San Francisco directory even lists an "environmental psychologist." While satisfactory reports on relatively simple projects have been conscientiously prepared by recent graduates of many of the newly instituted university programs in environmental resources, in many cases attempts to cut costs by hiring inexperienced students or self-proclaimed multi-disciplinary "environmental specialists" result in shoddy products and ultimate delays in approval.

The onslaught of so-called environmental experts has created difficulty and confusion for the unschooled developer, as well as the City Council, who must hire someone to prepare a report. One alternative that has been suggested is state licensing of persons deemed qualified for the task. The problem is that no one has yet determined precisely what qualifications are needed for the job! While a licensed sanitary engineer may be perfectly suited to prepare the section of an EIS which deals with sewage needs, he or she is no more likely to be able to discuss air quality, wildlife, or historic buildings than is the applicant whose project is being reviewed. Moreover, by limiting the field to licensed experts there may be a tendency to limit the scope of reports to those physically-oriented disciplines which are easiest to license. Although many jurisdictions lean toward a narrow definition of the term "environment," the National Environmental Policy Act, as noted earlier, emphasizes the total human environment. It appears, therefore, that the best approach to impact assessment may be the aforementioned team concept, with a generalist at the helm and specialists evaluating specific considerations. An increasing number of planning departments have taken this tack, augmenting their staffs of planning generalists with whatever economists, engineers, sociologists, biologists, and geologists the budget will allow.

CONCLUSION

EIS at the local level is at a crossroads. With the requirement of the Housing Act of 1974 that the local mayor, if he accepts Community Development funding, assume the responsibility of the Secretary of HUD in enforcing EIS requirements, we can go either of two ways. We can pursue at the local level a replication of the experience at the federal level—massive EIS's mandated by tortuous requirements, fulfilling uncoordinated objectives—the ultimate result being only marginally effective. Or we can attempt to relate environmental concern to both the local regulatory and planning processes—where the chances for success and equity are better, in our view.

If we impose costs on the developers, the added costs will come back to us as consumers. If we require government to absorb the costs, the costs come back to us as taxpayers. Reducing the cost of both private development and government regulation is a critical concern for all of us. We should not think that either public or private pocketbooks are simply a blank check for all of us to draw upon.

NOTES

1. See Harold F. Wise, "The Environmental Impact Statement and the Comprehensive Plan" in Robert W. Burchell and David Listokin, eds., *Future Land Use: Energy, Environmental, and Legal Constraints,* New Brunswick, N.J., Center for Urban Policy Research, 1975.

2. Burton C. Kross, "Preparation of an Environmental Impact Statement," *University of Colorado Law Review,* Vol. 44, 1972, p. 84.

3. James A. Roberts, "Just What is an Environmental Impact Statement," *Urban Land,* January 1974.

4. State of New Jersey, *Guidelines for Environmental Commissions,* Trenton, N.J., Department of Environmental Protection, 1974, Appendix I.

5. Norman Williams, Jr., *Land Use and the Police Power* (forthcoming), Chapter 5.

6. George Sternlieb, Robert W. Burchell, and James W. Hughes, "The Future of Housing and Urban Development" in Robert W. Burchell and David Listokin, eds., *Future Land Use: Energy, Environmental, and Legal Constraints,* New Brunswick, N.J., Center for Urban Policy Research,

1975.

7. See Paul H. Sedway, "The Environmental Impact Report"; Robert W. Twiss, "Linking EIS to the Planning Process"; and Harold F. Wise, "The Environmental Impact Statement and the Comprehensive Plan" in Robert W. Burchell and David Listokin, eds., *Future Land Use: Energy, Environmental, and Legal Constraints,* New Brunswick, N.J., Center for Urban Policy Research, 1975.

8. *Ibid.*

9. See Richard N.L. Andrews, "A Philosophy of Environmental Impact Assessment," *Journal of Soil and Water Conservation,* Vol. 28, 1972, p. 201.

10. See Donald G. Hagman, "NEPA's Progeny Inhabit the States—Were the Genes Defective?" *Urban Law Annual,* Vol. 7, 1974, p. 47.

11. *Ibid.*

12. Twiss, "Linking EIS"; Wise, "Environmental Impact Statement"; and Sedway, "Environmental Impact Report."

13. Sedway, *Ibid.*

14. University of Pennsylvania, Center for Ecological Research in Planning and Design, Medford, N.J.: *Performance Requirements for the Maintenance of Social Values Represented by the Natural Environment,* Philadelphia, 1974.

15. G. Nehman, N. Dee, J. Griffin and B. Cost, *Application of the Land Use Trade Off Model to Assess Land Use Capabilities of the Beaufort-Jasper County, S.C.,* Columbus, Ohio, Battelle Laboratories, 1974.

16. Rahenkamp, Sachs and Wells and Associates, *Revised Impact Zoning for the Town of Duxbury, Mass.,* Philadelphia, 1973.

17. See Candice M. Ashman and Peter W. Larson, *Municipal Land Use Decisions: The Tools, The Methods,* Bedminster, N.J., The Bedminster Township Environmental Commission and the Upper Raritan Watershed Association, 1975 (Forthcoming).

18. Hagman, "NEPA's Progeny," p. 55.

19. New Jersey Department of Community Affairs, Local Planning Assistance Unit, *The Environmental Assessment Requirement: A Guidance Document for 701 Participants,* Trenton, N.J., April 1974, 15 pp.

20. California Council on Intergovernmental Relations, *Guidelines for Local General Plans,* Sacramento, Calif., September 1973, Ch. 1-5.

21. Hagman, "NEPA's Progeny," p. 54.

ENVIRONMENTAL IMPACT STATEMENT GUIDELINES: RECOMMENDED PROCEDURE

INTRODUCTION

This chapter outlines an approach and format for preparing an environmental impact statement. The relationship between types of development and their environmental impacts are often not completely understood. For this reason, the approach given below attempts only to list the parts of the environment which can be affected by development, the natural processes through which those impacts can occur, and the types of information one would gather to analyze those impacts. In each case, sources are given for the environmental information which should be presented, the standards or criteria which have been established for certain types of pollution, and additional information on particular environmental impacts.

Current guidelines suggest that the impact statement include *separate* sections describing the impact of the environment on the project and the impact of the project on the environment. Since these impacts are closely interrelated, the guidelines below include discussion of both of these types of impacts under each environmental heading. The current guidelines of the appropriate agency should always be consulted, however, before proceeding with a draft EIS.

The guide is divided into the following sections:

   I. Description of the project
   II. Description of the existing environment
   III. Impacts of/on the environment
   IV. Internal project environment
   V. Alternative strategies
   VI. Unavoidable adverse impacts
   VII. Impacts over time
   VIII. Irreversible/irretrievable commitments

The emphasis of these sections should be tailored to the type and size of the project being proposed and the setting in which the development will take place. To illustrate how the EIS's might differ, one might divide projects into several categories: planned vs. unplanned, large vs. small, and urban vs. rural.

A large project is more likely to have a definitive plan and, because of its size, more potential impacts associated with it. Thus, one would expect the EIS to be more involved and more complete. There might, for example, be more significant impacts on soils resulting in large amounts of erosion and increased runoff into streams. In addition, a large project would tend to attract more secondary developments, such as service industries. Traffic generation would therefore be greater. On the other hand, a large development might, in certain instances, be better able to support mass transit thereby minimizing traffic and air pollution impacts. Finally, a large development will produce an internal environment, where a small one may not.

Following this same line of reasoning, one would expect the EIS for smaller projects to be less involved. Since fewer resource commitments will be made, lower impacts might be expected. Major exceptions will occur where a development is to be built on or near an area of critical environmental significance. Thus, even a small project might destroy a building of historical importance or part of a unique wildlife habitat. The size and location of the project will affect the nature of its impacts and thereby, the extensiveness of the EIS.

The EIS will also reflect the type of project which is being proposed and the types of environmental resources which are affected. In an urban area, for example, one would expect greater impacts on social, economic, and aesthetic conditions because the natural, physical environment has already been significantly altered. In a rural area, the social impacts may be just as important, but the physical impacts should be given more attention. Obviously, a project built adjacent to a stream or lake will have impacts on that water body, and the EIS will therefore be expanded in the sections on water quality and flooding. In contrast, a project removed from bodies of water will be less likely to produce those types of impacts.

Thus, the nature of an EIS can vary dramatically depending on the size, nature, and location of the proposed development. The guidelines presented here attempt to point out many of the potential impacts of all types of projects and the types of supporting evidence which will be required in writing an EIS. The question of evidence should deeply concern the EIS writer—sweeping statements about the nature of an environmental impact made without some supporting evidence often lead to delays in the review process.

I. DESCRIPTION OF THE PROJECT

I.A. Purpose of the project
What is the local need for development? What will be provided by development and how does the project answer local need?

I.B. Status of the project
Where is the project in the planning stages? What has actually been done thus far?

I.C. General location of the project
Show location within both the community and region as a whole, including a map for each. Show the relationship of the site to the nearest airport, major highways and roads, railroads, major recreation areas, and major centers of employment and shopping. Also show the relationship of the site to the rest of the community, county, state, and metropolitan area. Photos of the site might help illustrate the description. Aerial photographs at different scales are generally available through local and regional planning agencies, county and state tax assessors offices, and the U.S. Department of Agriculture, Agricultural Stabilization and Conservation Service.

II. DESCRIPTION OF THE EXISTING ENVIRONMENT

II.A. Physical environment
II.A.1. LAND AND CLIMATE
II.A.1.1. Soils
Three major processes affect the soil environment: erosion and sedimentation, mass wasting, and runoff. Development can greatly accelerate these processes, causing environmental damage. Thus, it is important to describe the site in terms of variables which can affect these processes. Another important set of soil variables derives from the capability of the soil to absorb urban uses with a minimum of economic and environmental cost.

Begin with a general description of the soils on the site. Descriptions can be derived from one or more of three classification systems, depending on how much information is available: the USDA system, the Unified System, and/or the AASHO system (references below). Soil variables of significance include texture, structure, permeability, bearing capacity, shrink-swell potential, depth to bedrock, rockiness, and depth to water table. The presence of soils with impermeable layers, referred to as fragipans or duripans (depending on their origin and composition) should also be noted.

The erosion process can be described by the soil loss equation:

$$A = RKLSCP$$

where
A = soil loss in tons/acre
R = rainfall factor
K = soil erodibility factor

L = slope length factor
S = slope gradient factor
C = cropping management or land use factor
P = erosion control practice factor

This equation attempts to predict the amount of soil which will erode from an area under varying physical conditions and land use and erosion control practices.

The factors R,L,S,C, and P are defined in the description of the existing environment under other subheadings, below. Soil erodibility is the tendency of soil to be transported by water. The "K" erodibility factor should be included as another variable describing the site, under the soils section. It varies theoretically between 0 (no soil loss) and 1 (complete soil loss) with most soils under natural conditions falling into the range of 0.17 to 0.49.

Soils are also rated on the amount of runoff to be expected. Hydrologic soil group ratings range from A (least runoff and greatest infiltration capacity) to D (most runoff and least infiltration capacity). The ratings are related to many of the physical parameters listed above by the U.S. Soil Conservation Service (SCS). They are important in evaluating the impact of a development on runoff and flooding.

Based on these parameters, a general evaluation can be made of the suitability of the soils on the site for different uses. Ratings of soil limitations can be defined in terms of degree as follows:

Slight—little or no limitation for a particular use
Moderate—some limitations for a particular use which can usually be overcome by careful design, but at greater cost (economic and environmental)
Severe—cannot usually be overcome without special and costly measures

Such ratings are given in recent soil survey reports or may be derived using guidelines established by SCS. The types of limitations which are discussed will depend on the nature of the project being proposed. For example, suitability for septic systems would not be considered in an area where only public sewerage systems are allowed. Examples of other suitability categories which might be evaluated include: agriculture, wildlife, woodland, foundations, roads, parking lots, play areas, and lawns.

A final detailed soil survey at the site would reveal the portion of the site which falls into the various soil categories. The developer and reviewer of the impact statement is then made aware of possible problems involved in construction and maintenance by area.

Sources of information on soil characteristics in an area include published soil surveys, the U.S. Soil Conservation Service, the local soil conservation district or cooperative extension office, and soil discriptions made for natural resource inventories of local or regional planning boards.

For further information:

American Association of State Highway Officials (AASHO), *Standard Specifications for Highway Materials and Methods of Sampling and Testing.* Washington, D.C., 1961.

Bartelli, L.J., *et al.*, *Soil Surveys and Land Use Planning.* Madison, Wis., Soil Science Society of America and American Society of Agronomy, 1966.

Beasley, R.P., *Erosion and Sediment Pollution Control.* Ames, Iowa, Iowa State University Press, 1972.

U.S. Department of Agriculture, Soil Survey Staff, Soil Conservation Service, *Soil Classification: A Comprehensive System, 7th Approximation.* Washington, D.C., U.S. Government Printing Office, 1960.

U.S. Department of Agriculture, Soil Conservation Service, *Guide for Interpreting Engineering Use of Soils.* Washington, D.C., U.S. Government Printing Office, 1971.

U.S. Federal Housing Administration, *Engineering Soil Classification for Residential Developments.* Washington, D.C., U.S. Government Printing Office, 1961.

II.A.1.2. Topography

Topography is important in assessing possible soil erosion, mass wasting (landslides, soil creep, etc.), effects of development on runoff, and potential aesthetic conflicts. Include information on general slope characteristics and evaluate the slope and grade of the site as maximum, minimum, or average. Attempt to categorize the entire site by the percent of land in acres falling within the following slope categories:

Slope %	Acres	Percent of Total
0 — 4%		
5 — 9%		
10 — 15%		
16 — 25%		
greater than 25%		
	Total Acreage	100%

This section should also contain information on slope length, for possible use in calculating soil loss and runoff. Slope calculations can be made using a method devised by Arthur N. Strahler (cited below) which uses a random sampling procedure and a topographic map to prepare a slope map. The map areas can then be calculated using a planimeter. (A planimeter is an instrument which automatically integrates the area of a map by tracing around its borders.) One should consult available state guidelines which may delimit critical impact areas as a function of slope. For example, in humid areas of the northeastern United States, the SCS uses 15 percent as a critical point beyond which the land should not be developed because of severe erosion and mass wasting hazards.

Sources of slope information include U.S. Geological Survey topographic sheets, soil surveys, state bureaus of geology, and planning agencies.

For further information:

Highway Research Board, *Landslides and Engineering Practice*, Highway Research Board Special Report 29. Washington, D.C., Highway Research Board, 1958.

Strahler, Arthur N., "Quantitative Slope Analysis," *Bulletin of the Geological Society of America*, Vol. 67, May 1956, pp. 571-596.

Wentworth, C.K., "A Simplified Method of Determining the Average Slope of Land Surfaces," *American Journal of Science*, 5th Series, Vol. 20, pp. 185-194.

II. A.1.3. Subsurface Conditions

Subsurface conditions affect the ability of the site to support structures, the provision of underground utilities (such as water, sewerage, and natural gas), the stability of the formation under the stress of an earthquake, and the ability of the rock to serve as a ground water aquifer.

An aquifer is a rock formation capable of holding and transmitting water. As such, an aquifer can be an important water supply source. An aquifer is supplied with water from its "recharge area"—the area at the surface where water is able to seep down into the aquifer. Development can affect an aquifer by covering over the recharge area with impervious buildings and parking areas or by discharging wastes into the ground.

The description of the site should contain the following geological information:

a. bedrock type and characteristics (structural type and size)
b. surface geology
c. mineral resources, such as sand, gravel, oil
d. geologic cross sections
e. presence and characteristics of geologic faults in the area
f. location of aquifers and their recharge areas
g. seismology readings where appropriate

Sources of geologic information: U.S. Geological Survey, state bureaus of geology, well records, and local water companies.

For further information:

Baldwin, H. L. and C. L. McGuinness, *A Primer on Ground Water.* Washington, D.C., U.S. Geological Survey, 1963.

Flawn, Peter T., *Environmental Geology.* New York, Harper & Row, 1970.

Todd, D.K., *Ground Water Hydrology.* New York, Wiley, 1959.

II.A.1.4. Natural Drainage/Special Conditions

Describe surface drainage conditions and the presence of streams, lakes, and marshes near the site. If the site drains into more than one stream or lake, indicate what portion of the site drains to each basin. This may be accomplished by mapping the drainage divides on a topographic map.

For surface water bodies, a general description should be given of existing water quality and flooding conditions. Water quality parameters are discussed below in the section on impacts. An indication should be given of the floodplain of all surface water bodies. Unfortunately, there are several definitions of floodplain given by different agencies. HUD distinguishes between the floodplain and the floodway. A floodway is the channel of a river or other watercourse and the adjacent land areas required to carry and discharge a flood of a given magnitude. Locations of the floodplain and floodway are being mapped for HUD by the U.S. Geological Survey in conjunction with the Federal Flood Insurance Program.

Also include data on the frequency of flooding. Generally, the probability of floods of different magnitudes is reported along with the highest flood on record.

Describe the present uses of each of the water bodies.These might include water supply, swimming, boating, fishing, transportation, or aesthetic uses. Water quality standards are directly related to the use of a water body. Examples of standards as they relate to use are given below in the section on water pollution.

Report any other special physical conditions relating to the site or the region not already covered. These might include hazards of earthquakes, landslides, subsidence, or other physical limitations. Also report on any unique physical or natural features in the area. These can include streams, geologic formations, caverns, or other natural features.

Sources of information on flooding include the U.S. Geological Survey's Surface Water Records, records of state bureaus of geology or environmental conservation; and local water agencies. Water quality data are available through the U.S. Geological Survey's Water Quality Records, state agencies, and local water companies and sewerage treatment plans.

For further information:

Izaak Walton League of America, *A Citizen's Guide to Clean Water*. Washington, D.C., 1973. Available through the U.S. Environmental Protection Agency, Washington, D.C.

Swenson, H.A. and H. L. Baldwin, *A Primer on Water Quality*. Washington, D.C., U.S. Geological Survey, 1965.

U.S. Department of Housing and Urban Development, *The National Flood Insurance Program*. Brochure. Washington, D.C., 1973.

U.S. Department of the Interior, U.S. Geological Survey, *Publications of the Geological Survey*. Washington, D.C., issued periodically.

U.S. Office of the Federal Register, *National Flood Insurance Program*. Title 24, Housing and Urban Development, Paragraph 1909.1. Washington, D.C., U.S. Government Printing Office, April 1, 1974.

II.A.1.5. Climatic Conditions

Local climatic conditions can have important effects on a development. For example, an unusually heavy fog can disrupt automobile traffic. Unusual storms can induce mudflows and other earth surface movements under particular conditions. Climatic conditions also affect the level and dispersion of air pollutants from different sources.

Major climatic characteristics include precipitation, temperature, and winds. Describe regional precipitation for the area around the site. Mean and/or median and maximum and minimum precipitation should be given for the entire year, for each month, and possibly for different seasons. The probability of the occurrence of storms of particular intensity and duration is another important set of parameters.

Describe regional temperature in the same manner as precipitation. Data on duration or range of temperatures above or below freezing might be included in this section. In certain areas, the frequency of occurrence of temperature inversions may be of significance. In inversion, a warm air mass overlays a colder mass near the ground producing stagnant air.

Other climatic information which should be presented include data on relative humidity and predominant wind speed and direction.

Describe any unusual climatic conditions such as intense fog, extremely high or low temperatures, strong wind and storm conditions, tornadoes, and hurricanes.

Sources of climatic information are available through the National Oceanic and Atmospheric Administration. University libraries often have the information for a particular area on file.

For further information:

Beals, Gordon A., *Guide to Local Diffusion of Air Pollutants*. Technical Report 214. Scott Air Force Base, Ill., U.S. Air Force, Air Weather

Service, 1971.

Detwyler, Thomas R., *Man's Impact on Environment.* New York, McGraw-Hill Book Co., 1971.

Epstein, A. H., *A Guide for Considering Air Quality in Urban Planning.* Washington, D.C., U.S. Environmental Protection Agency, Office of Air Quality Planning and Standards, 1974. Available through the National Technical Information Service (NTIS), Springfield, Va.

Landsberg, H.E., "The Climate of Towns" in William L. Thomas, Jr., ed., *Man's Role in Changing the Face of the Earth.* Chicago, Ill., University of Chicago Press, 1956.

II.A.2. VEGETATION AND WILDLIFE

Ecology is defined as the pattern of relationships between organisms and their environment. In defining the nature of a development site, reference has already been made to parts of the physical environment. It then remains to describe plant and animal species and communities. The complexities of ecosystems make this identification process a difficult task. Assessing the impacts of development on ecosystems is made even more difficult because the nature of the interrelationships among plants and animals in many ecosystems is poorly understood. Effects of ecosystem alteration are not linear, because natural biochemical cycles tend to concentrate certain types of materials. Disposing one unit of mercury, for example, can result in 1,000 units concentrated in the fatty tissue of certain fish.

Despite these types of problems, the natural community should be described in the process of writing an EIS. Generally, the vegetation communities in a land ecosystem constitute the first part of the description. For example, the predominant species types in the temperate deciduous forest are whiteoak, blackoak, shagbark hickory, and bitternut hickory. These trees represent the climax vegetation in this climate. The climax ecosystem is that mixture of plant and animal species which will inhabit an area if it is undisturbed for an adequate length of time. These climax species in this example are often mixed with smaller numbers of willows, cottonwoods, red maple, American elm, and other species of shrubs and trees.

Associated with a particular vegetation mixture are various animal species. Animals inhabit particular *niches* or places in the biotic community which are related to specific vegetation types or sources of food. For example, deer are one of the predominant species of the temperate forest because they feed on the leaves of the climax forest. Other common species in this community are black bear, gray fox, raccoon, and fox squirrel.

In a similar fashion, one can proceed to describe the species which are dominant on the development site. The level of detail used will vary according to the size of the project and the nature and relative importance of the local, natural ecosystem.

Another important consideration is whether or not any rare or endangered species are present in the area. As was discussed in previous chapters, contact with local conservation groups and state conservation agencies can be important steps in avoiding problems associated with failure to recognize the presence of important biological communities or species.

Sources of information on vegetation and wildlife resources include local conservation groups, state conservation agencies, and the U.S. Fish and Wildlife Service.

For further information:

Ehrenfeld, David W., *Biological Conservation*. New York, Holt, Rinehart, Winston, 1970.

International Union for the Conservation of Nature, *Red Data Books*. Morges, Switzerland, published annually. Gives up to date listing of rare and endangered species.

National Wildlife Federation, *Conservation Directory*. Washington, D.C., published annually.

Odum, Eugene P., *Fundamentals of Ecology*. Philadelphia, W.B. Saunders Company, 1971.

Shelford, Victor E., *The Ecology of North America*. Urbana, University of Illinois Press, 1963.

II.A.3. LAND USE

Describe the overall regional land use. List the specific breakdown of existing regional land use in acres and percents. A possible classification scheme would include the following categories.

    a. Residential
    b. Industrial
    c. Commercial
    d. Public and quasi-public
    e. Open space
    f. Water and swamp
    g. Vacant
    h. Other

Describe density, lot size, and other area zoning requirements. A map illustrating the above classifications would be useful, especially if the study area is large.

Information on land use is available through local planning agencies. In addition, certain areas employ tax mapping systems which give up to date information on land use and property values. Some states have developed or are in the processing of implementing land information systems which give data on such things as land use, natural resources, water and sewer lines, and location of public facilities. Examples of such systems include the Land Use and Natural Resources Inventory (LUNR) in New York State and the Land Oriented Resource Data System (LORDS) in New Jersey.

For further information:

Chapin, F. Stuart, *Urban Land Use Planning*. New York, Harper and Row, 1957.

New Jersey Bureau of Geology, *Land Oriented Resource Data System*. Trenton, N.J., Bureau of Geology, Department of Environmental Protection, 1974.

New York State Office of Planning Services, *LUNR, What It is and How It is Used*. Albany, New York, State Office of Planning Services, 1972.

II.A.4. INFRASTRUCTURE
II.A.4.1. Water Supply

Describe sources of water supply, such as wells, reservoirs, or surface water sources.

Locate water sources on reference map.

Discuss whether public or private individuals and companies or perhaps a combination of these provide water supplies.

Comment on short and long term water supply. With reference to wells, note depth, present and safe yield either in gallons per minute or millions of gallons per day. (Safe yield is the rate of diversion or extraction for consumptive use that can be indefinitely extracted from surface and groundwater systems within the limits of economic feasibility and under specific conditions of water supply development.)

In discussing reservoirs, list overflow elevation above sea level and capacity. The latter is generally assumed to equal twice the maximum one-day usage.

For surface water sources, note the safe yield, the capacity of any treatment facilities, and the condition and extent of the distribution system. the distribution system should also be discussed for other sources of supply, along with any differences in the quality of raw water from various sources.

List daily average water usage. Note also peak demand, particularly utilization during summer months. Peak demand can be discussed in terms of daily and seasonal demand for drinking water and in terms of instantaneous demand for water required for fire fighting.

Compare demand to present capacity.

Information on water supply sources, quantities, quality, and distribution can usually be obtained from public or private officials responsible for water supply. Information on the safe yields and quality of ground water resources

is generally available through the state bureau of geology.
For further information:

Linaweaver, F. P., Jr., John C. Geyer, and Jerome B. Wolff, *A Study of Residential Water Use.* Washington, D.C., U.S. Government Printing Office, 1967.

II.A.4.2. Sewerage/Septic Systems

Include a general description of the sewage disposal system. Does the system consist of private septic systems, a public sewer line and treatment facility, or a combination of the two? If the system is public, it is important to note whether the system consists of separate sanitary and storm sewers or whether these two systems are combined. Combined systems tend to overload during storms, precluding sewage treatment.

Another important aspect of the sewer system relates to type of treatment. Note the type of treatment process which is used in both public and private systems. For public systems, locate the sewer lines near the development site and note their capacity and present usage rate. Also, indicate the present capacity and average load at the sewage treatment plant.

Finally, investigate the policies and relationships of public and private bodies responsible for sewage treatment and any proposals for improvement of the present system.

Sources of information on sewer facilities include public and private sewer authorities, departments of health, local engineers, and state health and conservation departments.

For further information:

American Public Works Association, *Problems of Combined Sewer Facilities and Overflows: 1967.* FWPCA Pub. No. WP-20-11. Washington, D.C., Federal Water Pollution Control Agency, 1967.

Fair, Gordon M., J. C. Geyer, and D. A. Okum, *Water and Wastewater Engineering, Vol. 2: Water Purification and Wastewater Treatment and Disposal.* New York, John Wiley & Sons, 1968.

Goldstein, Steven N. and Walter J. Moberg, Jr., *Wastewater Treatment Systems for Rural Communities.* Washington, D.C., Commission on Rural Water, 1973.

II.A.4.3. Solid Waste

Describe the agencies responsible for solid waste management and their relationship to each other.

Specify the nature of the solid waste collection system. This may include landfill or dump facilities, transfer stations, resource recovery facilities (recycling processes), and incineration facilities. Methods and frequency of collection are also important. The capacity of each of the intermediate and final disposal facilities should be indicated along with the current levels of usage and costs for transportation and facility operation.

Other significant problems with the existing solid waste disposal system should be noted. These might include problems of odor, water pollution, and aesthetics near dump sites or air pollution problems associated with incineration.

Sources of this information are private and public garbage haulers, local health departments, and state departments of health and conservation.

For further information:

University of California, Sanitary Engineering Research Laboratory, *Comprehensive Studies of Solid Waste Management, Annual Report Number 3*. Berkeley, University of California, Sanitary Engineering Research Laboratory, 1971.

U.S. Environmental Protection Agency, Office of Solid Waste Management Programs, *First Report to Congress on Resource Recovery and Source Reduction, 3d ed.* Washington, D.C., U.S. Government Printing Office, 1974.

II.A.4.4. Drainage

Describe and locate existing drainage infrastructure. A map of storm sewers would aid this discussion. Note the type and age of the storm sewer system and the demands being placed on it. The existence of any overloaded drainage facilities in the vicinity of the development site is of great importance.

For further information:

Antoine, L.H., "Drainage and the Best Use of Urban Land," *Public Works*, Vol. 95, No. 2, February 1964, pp. 88-90.

II.A.4.5. Energy Resources

Describe energy resources in the area, listing different local and regional authorities and companies. These should include all energy suppliers—electricity, natural gas, and oil suppliers. Locate the nearest electric substations and note whether they are interlocking. Comment on existing energy demand versus capacity, noting whether there have been blackouts, brownouts, or similar occurrences.

Contact local companies to ascertain whether supplies are available for new customers and whether large users of energy will be moving into the region near the development site.

II.A.4.6. Transportation

Describe transportation and parking facilities in the area including:

a. Highways and feeder roads

b. Mass transit
c. Parking facilities
d. Location of other transportation infrastructure (Service and gas stations, mass transit service garages, etc.)

List and locate existing regional arteries. The nature of these roads, including such characteristics as interstate or state highway maintenance, multilane versus single lane construction, and speed limits. Stress highway travel time during rush hours and other periods to major employment centers. Note the theoretical capacity of existing and feeder highways (such as vehicles per hour (vph) that can be safety accommodated), as well as their present usage (average vph, rush hour vph). Where appropriate discuss proposed plans to expand regional road capacity. Report any recent studies of the origin and destination of trips and the number and types of trips made by residents of the area.

Describe and locate any mass transit facilities. Note their capacity, current usage, and the areas serviced. Briefly evaluate the quality of existing mass transit service considering the percentage of the population in the service area, convenience and number of stations and bus stops, frequency of service, and general comfort and convenience of the facilities.

Plans for expanding existing mass transit facilities and the details of such proposed activity should be described.

Discuss and locate on- and off-site parking capacity. Note the ratio of on- to off-site spaces as well as any existing parking problems.

Describe other transportation facilities including airports, heliports, ferries, and so forth.

For further information:

Ford, B. M., W. J. Roester, and M. C. Waddel, *Parametric Analysis of Generic Urban Transit Systems*. Baltimore, Johns Hopkins University Press, 1969.

Highway Research Board, National Research Council, *The Highway Capacity Manual*. Washington, D.C., 1960.

Krueckeberg, Donald A., and Arthur L. Silvers, *Urban Planning Analysis Methods and Models*. New York, John Wiley, 1974.

Meyer, J. R., J. F. Kain, and M. Wohl, *The Urban Transportation Problem*. Cambridge, Mass., Harvard University Press, 1965.

Oi, W. Y., and P. W. Shuldiner, *An Analysis of Urban Travel Demands*. Evanston, Ill., Northwestern University Press, 1962.

U.S. Department of Transportation, Federal Highway Administration, Bureau of Public Roads, *Guidelines for Trip Generation Analysis*.

EXHIBIT 6-1

EXAMPLE OF AMBIENT AIR QUALITY STANDARDS

Standards (micrograms per cubic meter)

Pollutant	Annual Arith. Mean	Max. 24 Hr. Concentration	Max 8 Hr. Concentration	Max 1 Hr. Concentration
Sulphur Dioxide (SO_2)	80	364	—	—
Particulates	75[1]	260	—	—
Carbon Monoxide (CO)	—	—	10	40
Photochemical Oxidants	—	—	—	160
Hydrocarbons (HC)	—	—	—	160[2]
Nitrogen dioxide (NO_2)	100	—	—	—

1. Annual Geometric Mean.
2. Max. 3 hr. concentration.

Source: *Code of Federal Regulations*, Title 40: Protection of Environment. Washington, U.S. Government Printing Office, 1973.

Washington, D.C., June 1967.

II.A.5. AIR POLLUTION

Air pollution levels in an area are related to the quantity of pollutants discharged into the air from various sources and the degree to which they are dispersed by mixing of the air. Models of air pollution attempt to approximate the quantity of pollution from sources by relating emissions to land use categories. Then, local climatic conditions are taken into account in estimating dispersion of the pollutants using complex mathematical models.

In defining the nature of air pollution in an area, one should describe the concentration levels for a number of variables. These are listed below along with an example of U.S. Environmental Protection Agency guidelines for levels which should be maintained in a healthy environment. (See exhibit 6-1.) EPA has also established regulations for the amount of emissions from particular sources. Automobile emissions are the best known of these, although the agency has also established standards for sources such as incinerators, power plants, and industrial heating systems. Actual standards may vary in particular localities.

Describe the daily average, eight-hour average, and maximum concentrations of air pollutants found in the development site area. Identify the major sources of air pollutants in the area—industries, residences, commercial enterprises, institutions, transportation systems, power plants, and incinerators. Include in the discussion any examples of special conditions which might affect air pollution problems. These might include a high frequency of temperature inversions, and problems of poor air circulation resulting from peculiar geographic conditions. Also note any tree or crop damage related to impure air.

Sources of air pollution information are local health agencies, regional offices of the U.S. Environmental Protection Agency, and state health and conservation departments.

II.A.6. NOISE POLLUTION

Sound levels are measured in decibels. One decibel is approximately equal to the threshhold of hearing in man.

In order to establish a base to which noise levels in a new development can be compared, one must first establish the *ambient* noise level. This is the background noise in an area before development takes place. Because of the instantaneous variations in noise, the ambient level must be established using a procedure of sampling over time. Readings are generally taken using a meter approved by the American National Standards Instutite. Readings are taken in db(A) values (decibels using an "A" weighting factor on the meter) since this type of reading is thought to most closely approximate human ear response. Ambient levels are established by taking readings at 10 second intervals for a period of 5 to 10 minutes, at different sites, during different times of the day. The sites selected for sampling should relate to areas of probable impact on the development, or impact of the development on the area. Times of the day for sampling will vary according to changes in the noise levels in a particular area. For example, higher noise levels will occur during rush hours on a busy street. Noise levels near a warehouse area will differ significantly on days when the warehouses are not in operation.

An alternative to establishing the ambient level is to calculate a project's *noise exposure*. This is a combination of noise level (in decibels) and duration. This type of measurement is currently required by the Federal Department of Transportation, the Federal Aviation Administration, and HUD. Specific guidelines for EIS relating to noise should be consulted before a decision is made on a methodology for taking noise readings.

As with air pollution, noise levels vary with the sources of the noise. These sources should be indicated. Noise standards have been established by several agencies. HUD circular 1390.2, *Noise Abatement and Control: Departmental Policy, Implementation Responsibilities, and Standards*, establishes noise criteria based on the noise exposure forecast for residential construction. For example, these guidelines list as acceptable for sleeping quarters noise levels which do not exceed 55 db(A) for more than an accumulation of 60 minutes in any 24 hours period. EPA has also established noise guidelines for particular noise sources.

It is important to consult with local health agencies, state agencies responsible for noise abatement, the EPA regional office, or the HUD regional office to ascertain what noise regulations apply in a particular area.

For further information:

Bragdon, Clifford, *Noise Pollution*. Philadelphia, University of Pennsylvania Press, 1971.

II.A.7. WATER POLLUTION

A characterization should be made of existing water quality for all of the water bodies (previously defined) located near the site. Numerous parameters may be employed in such an analysis including:

a. Fecal coliforms
b. Turbidity
c. Dissolved oxygen (DO)
d. Biochemical oxygen demand (BOD)
e. Inorganic carbon
f. Nitrate nitrogen
g. Total phosphates
h. pH
i. Temperature
j. Toxic substances

Each of these parameters will vary over time and space. Thus, one should indicate the time period, location, and frequency of all water readings taken or data gathered from other sources. Comparison between the existing water quality and water quality standards should be made. Standards are usually of two types: quality levels for water in existing bodies, which reflect how the water is used, and quality standards for the water discharged by water users into existing water bodies.

For example, standards relating to the quality of a river are related to whether it is used for drinking, swimming, fishing, or navigation. Propogation of fish will have the highest quality standards. An example of standards based on use is shown in exhibit 6-2.

Standards for discharge sources are related to the specific uses of the water before it is discharged or to national effluent standards. For example, standards for sewage treatment plants will be different from those for an oil refinery. For most residential developments these types of standards will not apply.

Sources of water quality data include local water companies, state health and environmental agencies, and regional offices of the EPA.

II.A.8. OTHER PHYSICAL CHARACTERISTICS

Discuss any other existing physical characteristics of the area which might have an impact on the project or on which the project may have an impact .

II.B. Social Environment
II.B.1. COMMUNITY FACILITIES

For each community activity servicing the site and immediate area, the following information should be provided:

a. General description
b. Location
c. Responsible body
d. Capacity
e. Existing demand
f. Relation of capacity to existing demand

The community services that should be analyzed should include:

a. Schools
b. Public safety and health
c. Recreation and culture

II.B.1.1. Schools

The overall nature and structure of the local school system should be described including the total number of schools, the educational track breakdown (for example, are there regional high schools, are there middle schools, and precisely which grades are the different schools servicing)

EXHIBIT 6-2

EXAMPLE OF AMBIENT WATER QUALITY STANDARDS

Standards for use for:

Parameters	Livestock	Freshwater Aquatic	Public Water Supply	Recreation
pH	—	6-9	5-9	6.5-8.3
Alkalinity	—	75% of Natural	—	—
BOD	—	—	0.5 mg/l	—
Mercury	1.0 mg/l[1]	0.2 mg/l	0.002 mg/l	—
Lead	0.1 mg/l	0.03 mg/l	0.05 mg/l	—

1. milligrams per liter.

Source: *Comparison of NTAC, NAS, and Proposed EPA Numerical Criteria for Water Quality.* Washington, D.C., U.S. Environmental Protection Agency, 1973.

pending school consolidations, and local versus state responsibility for funding schools.

Provide the exact location of all local schools and other pertinent bodies, such as the local Board of Education.

Identify the primary body responsible for local schools, as well as possible higher levels of authority and supervision, such as the State Department of Education.

The pupil capacity of the existing physical plant by elementary, middle, and high schools should be noted. Discuss firm plans for expansion or improvement and the likelihood of such activity.

Comment on existing demand in terms of number of children that will attend local public schools. Relate projected demand to present capacity.

Note any current problems with financing associated with the school system.

II.B.1.2. Health and Safety

Describe the nature of existing services relating to health and safety. These include medical facilities and personnel and fire and police protection. Health services should be described in terms of the number of existing hospitals, the services they offer, their capacity, and present use; any health clinics which might be of significance to the residents or users of any new development; the number and distribution of physicians; and the nature of emergency health care facilities such as ambulances and emergency rooms. Comment on the present adequacy of these facilities and services for the existing population.

Describe fire protection in the area. Indicate the number of fire fighting units, whether they are volunteer or professional, the amount of existing equipment, and financing for the fire departments. In light of the current number of fire emergencies, comment on the adequacy of these facilities.

Discuss police protection in the area. Note the sizes and jurisdictions of police personnel and any existing problems with crime in the area.

Describe the social services available locally. Indicate what types of services are available and how many people are served. Comment on the adequacy of services for the existing population.

Information on these services is generally available through local officials and state agencies.

II.B.1.3. Recreation and Culture

Describe the nature of existing facilities for recreational and cultural activities. Indicate the size, capacity, and types of facilities in all parks. List the number of types of other recreational and cultural facilities such as movie theaters, concert halls, gymnasiums, public ice skating or swimming facilities, etc. Note the capacity of each facility (where applicable) and current rates of use.

Comment on the adequacy of recreational facilities in the area. Several alternative sets of standards for recreation facilities have been established.

Consult with local planning officials or state parks and recreation officials for further information.

II.B.2. EMPLOYMENT

List major regional industrial and commercial facilities servicing the site and the area. Note the relative numbers of persons employed at each site and discuss where people live relative to their place of employment.

List and locate planned major regional industrial and commercial plants.

Discuss community and regional employment levels. Note employment and unemployment trends. Note any declines or increases in the total number of jobs or any major changes in the types of employment available in the region.

Employment information is usually available through local chambers of commerce and state employment agencies.

II.B.3. SOCIOECONOMIC CHARACTERISTICS

The variables which are generally utilized to describe the socioeconomic characteristics of an area are derived in part from the field of social area analysis. (See references below.) This theory maintains that social structure can be defined in terms of economic status, family status, and ethnic status. One need not necessarily employ the techniques used in social area analysis in an impact statement. However, the same types of variables should be described in the EIS.

The economic status of an area can be described in terms of its economic base (as described in the Ullman monograph below) and a number of other economic indicators.

Describe general community population characteristics including:

a. Population size
b. Population change

Discuss changes in population characteristics over the last two decennial censuses, including socioeconomic and racial characteristics:

a. Racial and ethnic composition
b. Age breakdown
c. Education
d. Occupation
e. Income
f. Housing composition

It may sometimes be useful to discuss other variables, such as community history, political changes, changing economic or social functions, or to view the variables in a regional perspective.

Discuss any changes in industrial composition and business characteristics not covered in the employment section.

EXHIBIT 6-3

CHECKLIST OF POSSIBLE AESTHETIC RESOURCES

____ Rock outcroppings, ridges, cliffs, hills, mountains, or valleys

____ Forest, wild flowers, meadows, or marsh land

____ Bodies of water, shorelines, waterfalls, or islands

____ Well-maintained farmsteads, pasture, filled land, crops, or orchards

____ Cityscapes, civic buildings, churches, squares

____ Harbor scenes

____ Historic buildings, distinctive structures

____ Milestone, historic road markers

____ Covered bridges, other bridges

____ Canals and locks

____ Old country cemeteries, old stone walls

____ Monuments

____ Dams, reservoirs

____ Golf courses, landscaped areas

____ Trails

____ Long, distant, open view

____ Broad, wide, open view

____ Treelined right-of-way

____ High degree of visual variety

Source: *Cayuga County Highway Improvement Program, Phase II: An Initial Set of Highway Improvement Priorities.* Auburn, N.Y., Cayuga County Planning Board, 1974.

Sources of data on population are the U.S. Census, local and regional planning agencies, state departments of commerce, and bureaus of vital statistics.

For further information:

Hughes, James, *Urban Indicators, Metropolitan Evolution and Public Policy*. New Brunswick, N.J., Rutgers University, Center for Urban Policy Research, 1972.

Tiebout, C., *The Community Economic Base Study*, Supplementary Paper No. 16. New York, Committee for Economic Development, 1962.

Ullman, E., M. Dacey, and H. Brodsley, *The Economic Base of American Cities*. Seattle, University of Washington Press, 1969.

II.C. Aesthetic Environment

Evaluation of the aesthetic environment is a very subjective task. Nevertheless, it remains important to describe the general aesthetic features of an area—and their significance to the local community—in analyzing environmental impacts.

Discuss general aesthetic features including the overall natural landscape, architectural style of existing buildings, existing landscaping, and similar features.

Historic and archeological sites and architecturally significant properties including those listed in or being considered for nomination to the National Register of Historic Places should also be discussed.

The checklist in exhibit 6-3 gives a more complete idea of the types of natural and cultural features which might have aesthetic significance. Comment on the presence of any of these aesthetic elements.

III. IMPACTS OF/ON THE ENVIRONMENT

III.A. Physical Environment
III.A.1. LAND AND CLIMATE
III.A.1.1. Soils

Using the capability maps produced for the first section in describing the environment, discuss the site plan and design with regard to the location of both major utilities and structural improvements. Are there significant areas of the site that will not support the proposed development in terms of bearing capacity, depth to bedrock, propensity for soil movement, or other soil factors?

Will the soils be able to support the vegetation—trees, grass, or other shrubbery—planned for the site or will topsoil need to be brought in from elsewhere? If septic tank sewage disposal is contemplated, comment on the capability of the soils to absorb the wastes and how these capabilities have affected the site design.

Comment on the overall plan according to the degree of soil limitations for all other uses discussed in the first section. Are soil conditions on the site likely to make safe development costly?

Are there any special conditions which have affected or might affect the use of the site? For example, certain areas of alluvial soil along the Potomac River are subject to sliding when the natural balance of the ground is disturbed. This could result in a complete house or apartment building sliding downslope.

Having described the impacts of the soils on the project, comment on the impact of the project on the soils. To what degree will the sediment yield from the area increase during construction and in the long run? Project sediment yield using one of the methods sited below. Might the soil become compacted during and after construction? The amount of compaction will significantly affect runoff in the area.

Calculate the runoff changes which will occur due to the urbanization of the area. Several methods are available for doing this, using data on the existing soils and information about the design of the project. (See references below.) These runoff figures can then be used to estimate any impacts the project may have on peak streamflow and flooding.

Discuss efforts which will be made by the developer to mitigate negative soil impact. How long will bare soil be exposed? Will the topsoil be replaced to the same depth as before construction took place? Will any actions be taken to minimize soil erosion by wind and water during and after construction is completed? What efforts will be made to stabilize cut banks and other slopes? Will any water be retained on site in holding ponds in order to mitigate effects of runoff?

For further information:

Beasley, R.P., *Erosion and Sediment Pollution Control*. Ames, Iowa, Iowa State University Press, 1972.

Hammer, Thomas R., *Impact of Urbanization on Peak Streamflow*, Discussion Paper No. 63. Philadelphia, Regional Service Research Institute, 1973.

Ingles, O. G. and J. B. Metcalf, *Soil Stabilization*. New York, John Wiley and Sons, 1973.

Strahler, Arthur N., "Quantitative Analysis of Watershed Geomorphology," *Transactions of the American Geophysical Union*, Vol. 38, 1957, pp. 913-920.

U.S. Department of Agriculture, Soil Conservation Service, *SCS National Engineering Handbook, Section 4, Hydrology*. Washington, D.C., U.S. Government Printing Office, 1972.

Wolman, M. G. and P. A. Schick, "Effects of Construction on Fluvial Sediment, Urban and Suburban Areas of Maryland," *Water Resources Research*, Vol. 3, No. 2, 1962, pp. 451-462.

III.A.1.2. Topography

Discuss whether site topography will restrict construction. Using the slope maps prepared for the site description, describe the relationship of the design to the topographic conditions. Comment on any relevant state or other legislation prohibiting or curtailing building on sites with special topographical features. These include restrictions based on slope percent and other special land use controls imposed on scenic areas, in coastal areas, and adjacent to rivers.

Discuss any opportunities presented by the existing topography which could improve the overall aesthetic impacts of the project. For example, the residents of the new building may enjoy a scenic view because of the topographic position of buildings at the site.

Discuss any special problems resulting from topographic considerations. Will the grade of the resulting access roads be so steep as to cause problems of access in the winter months? Will access be restricted to motor vehicles because of the slope, or will bicycles and pedestrians be able to get there? Describe any problems of slope stabilization which have affected the design.

Discuss the impacts the project will have on the topography. Especially important is whether any major earth moving activities will greatly alter the topography and what effects this alteration may have on soil loss and sedimentation, scenic value, and runoff. Will any relocation of drainage divides take place in the process of construction? Will topographic alterations result in any adverse microclimatic changes? For example, removal of a small hill may result in an increase in wind on the site, causing snow drifting problems in the winter.

Discuss any actions planned to minimize any adverse effects.

For further information:

Black, Peter E., "Interrelationships of Forest, Soils, and Terrain in Watershed Planning," in Donald R. Coates, ed., *Environmental Geomorphology*. Binghamton, N.Y., State University of New York at Binghamton, Publications in Geomorphology, 1970.

Bryson, Reid A. and John E. Ross, "The Climate of the City," in Thomas R. Detrogler and Melvin G. Marcus, eds., *Urbanization and Environment*. Belmont, Calif., Duxbury Press, 1972.

III.A.1.3. Subsurface Conditions

Based on the identification of the surface and bedrock geology of the site, and the propensity for the occurrence of mass wasting, comment on whether certain construction techniques will be followed to conform to geologic conditions. For example, blasting may be necessary instead of excavation.

Discuss whether there are any construction prohibitions or requirements because of areal geologic conditions, such as faults, landslides, or mudflows. If such standards are present, outline how they will be satisfied.

Describe any special engineering practices which will be used. For example, different rock bases will require various foundation types. Also, note whether the geologic conditions will affect the location or costs of utility lines and roads serving the site.

The impacts of the project on subsurface conditions can be derived from the same basic information. Comment on whether the project will alter portions of geologic cross sections. In particular, note whether the stability of the formations might be disturbed. This will vary with the construction method (for example, blasting vs. excavation), the extent of construction activity, the nature of the geologic formation (rock types), and the arrangement of the rock layers.

Discuss alteration of any unique geologic features and depletion of any subsurface mineral resources.

Comment on the project impact on aquifer recharge. The extent of this impact will depend on the proportion of the recharge area which will be covered by impervious surface. Also note whether the quality of the ground water might be affected by sewage disposal or urban runoff waters. If a new ground water supply will be tapped for use in the development, investigate how water removal might affect subsidence, or sinking, of the area.

The source, severity, and duration of each of the possible impacts should be specified. In many cases, quantitative estimation of severity and duration will be difficult, so that only a qualitative discussion will be possible. In other cases, such as with the effect on aquifer recharge, a more quantitative analysis of the impacts will be feasible.

Discuss any actions which will be taken to ameliorate the environmental damage and the relationship of such actions to official local and area-wide planning.

For further information:

American Public Works Association, *Water Pollution Aspects of Urban Runoff*. Report to Federal Water Pollution Control Administration, No. WP 20-15. Washington, D.C., 1969.

Flawn, Peter T., *Environmental Geology*. New York, Harper & Row, 1970.

Poland, J. F. and G. H. Davis, "Land Subsidence Due to Withdrawal of Fluids," in Thomas R. Detwyler, ed., *Man's Impact on Environment*. New York, McGraw Hill Book Co., 1971.

Zaruba, Quido and Voztech Mendl, *Landslides and Their Control*. New York, Elsevier, 1969.

III.A.1.4. Special Conditions

Discuss whether construction will be prohibited or restricted because of special conditions, including dangers of mudslide, landslide, runoff, soil subsidence, construction on flood plains, earthquake, and interference with subsurface transmission and communication lines and rights-of-way.

Discuss any other impact the above conditions will have on the project, such as driving piles to minimize soil subsidence or building dykes to minimize flood dangers.

Comment on the effect of special conditions on the residents and users of the proposed development.

Discuss the impact of the project on special conditions at the site including flood plains, unique landscape, potential for mudslide, landslide, subsidence or earthquake, aerial or underground transmission lines and right-of-way.

Describe any other special conditions related to the physical environment which will have an impact on the project or which will lead to an impact of the project on the environment.

III.A.1.5. Climatic Conditions

Comment on whether heavy precipitation will require special attention to avoid flooding. This will be related to the probability of rainstorms of a particular intensity and duration and the likelihood of tornadoes and hurricanes.

Describe any other special project modifications that will have to be made because of local climatic conditions. These might include extensive lighting in areas of heavy fog, special windbreaks in windy areas to prevent erosion and snow drift, or uses of particular construction materials in areas susceptible to hurricanes, extremes of temperature, or high wind.

Discuss any efforts which have been made in the design to increase the project's compatability with the microclimate. For example, orientation of the buildings might maximize the sunlight while avoiding heat loss from openings which face prevailing winds.

Describe whether local temperature conditions will require particular project heating and cooling systems, such as extensive air conditioning in hot climates. Comment on whether local extremes of heat or cold will affect the pace and strategy of construction.

Describe how climatic conditions will affect the residents and users of the site.

Small projects will not usually have significant impacts on microclimatic conditions. However, under certain circumstances, the local microclimate may be affected. For example, if a large amount of traffic is generated by a project, the air pollutants may filter out sunlight, increase the amount of cloudiness and fog, and disturb the life cycles of plants and animals. Topographic modifications might affect local winds, as will removal of large numbers of trees. Large buildings themselves will alter air circulation in a local area. In addition, paving over large areas will tend to increase the local

Exhibit 6-3A
Land Use and Housing Sources: A Selected List

Anderson, Robert M., *American Law of Zoning: Zoning, Subdivision Control, Planning*. Rochester, New York, The Lawyers Cooperative Publishing Company, 1968.

Association of Bay Area Governments, *Development Regulations in Housing Costs—Supplementary Report*. Berkeley, California, 1970.

Babcock, Richard F., *The Zoning Game*. Madison, Wisconsin, University of Wisconsin Press, 1966.

Burchell, Robert W. with James W. Hughes, *Planned Unit Development: New Communities American Style*. New Brunswick, N.J., Center for Urban Policy Research, Rutgers University, 1972.

Chapin, Jr., F. Stuart, *Urban Land Use Planning*. Urbana, Ill., University of Illinois Press, 1965.

Clawson, Marion, *Suburban Land Conversion in the United States*. Baltimore, Johns Hopkins Press for Resources for the Future, Inc., 1971.

Gaffney, Mason and Richard F. Muth, *Land as an Element of Housing Costs: The Effects of Public Policies and Practices, the Effects of Housing Demand*. Arlington, Virginia, Institute for Defense Analyses, 1968.

Goodman, William I. and Freund, Eric C., *Principles and Practices of Urban Planning*. Washington, D.C., International City Managers Association, 1968.

Mandelker, Daniel R., *The Zoning Dilemma: A Legal Strategy for Urban Change*. Indianapolis, Bobbs-Merrill, 1971.

Muth, Richard F. and Elliot Wetzler, *Effects of Constraints on Single-Unit Housing Costs*. Arlington, Virginia, Institute of Defense Analyses, 1968.

Sagalyn, Lynne B. and George Sternlieb, *Zoning and Housing Costs*. New Brunswick, N.J., Center for Urban Policy Research, Rutgers University, 1972.

Williams, Jr., Norman, *American Planning Law: Land Use and the Police Power*. Forthcoming, 1975.

temperature because asphalt and concrete absorb more solar heat than does natural vegetation.

Comment on whether the project might have any impacts on local microclimate.

III.A.2. VEGETATION AND WILDLIFE

Discuss whether existing or planned parks and other protected areas will constrain present or future project development. Describe any special design features which have been incorporated into the site plan in order to help preserve the natural vegetation and species habitats.

Comment on how the local vegetation, wildlife, and natural areas will affect both the residents and users of the proposed project. Natural areas may in fact enhance the residential quality of a development, serve as a buffer zone for noncompatible land uses, and maintain the natural balance in an area.

Describe the possible impacts of the project on fauna and flora on the site and in the area. Based on the description of the ecosystem given previously, note what types of vegetation and wildlife will be directly impacted by the project. Also discuss any secondary impacts resulting from construction noise, sedimentation, microclimatic alteration, or changes in species composition. Pay particular attention to any habitat destruction or other activities which will have an impact on rare and endangered species.

Where appropriate, comment on measures, such as replanting, resodding, landscaping, or retaining animal breeding areas, taken to minimize harm to existing and future vegetation, and wildlife.

If there are local and area planning efforts to preserve vegetation and wildlife species, discuss how the project's impact (and measures to reduce adverse effects) relate to such planning activities.

III.A.3. LAND USE

Comment on how existing land use statutes influence project development and configuration. To illustrate, mixed residential-commercial units may be built because of a local PUD zone. Note whether a zoning variance is planned.

Discuss how existing zoning requirements may affect project cost. Minimum lot size, interior space, and frontage requirements may all influence development and construction costs.

Comment on whether existing land use statutes (for example, PUD zones) will influence project timing and phasing.

Note how local land use requirements will affect the expected residents or users of the proposed project. To illustrate, statutes prohibiting or limiting local commercial development may force project residents to travel to regional shopping areas.

Comment on whether the project will parallel or will differ from existing land use patterns. Is the project a multi-family unit in a region of single-family residences, or will it have higher population density than surrounding developments?

Discuss the severity of this impact and how it relates to official local and area-wide planning. Also discuss any secondary land use impacts resulting from the project. For example, a large residential development will attract service industries, such as shopping areas and gas stations. Discuss also how these possible secondary impacts relate to official local and area-wide plans.

III.A.4. INFRASTRUCTURE
III. A.4.1. Water Supply

Discuss whether local water availability is likely to restrain size, landscaping, or other features of the project, now or in the future.

Note whether on-site pumping stations will have to be built, wells dug, or pipeline laid to meet the development's needs.

Describe what impact local water charges will have on the monthly housing cost.

Discuss the impact of local water supply on the residents and users of the proposed development. This might include references to limitations on total use, if any, and problems with the quality of the local water supply.

In order to calculate impact of the project on water supply, the proposed development's water need must be projected. This can be done by obtaining a local per capita water consumption figure and then multiplying this per capita use by the development's population. A longer but more accurate method is to project water usage of different components of the development—industrial, commercial, institutional, public, and most important, residential.

Industrial water use at the project can be derived by using the industrial water use coefficients in terms of gallons per day per employee derived by Hittman Associates. These coefficients are broken down by SIC code. (See exhibit 6-4.)

The development's commercial water use can also be calculated using Hittman coefficients. To illustrate, Hittman estimates a water utilization rate of 0.106 gallons per day per square foot of sales space footage.

Institutional, public, and unaccounted for demands can be derived by using a Hittman coefficient of 20.0 gallons per capita daily. Another approach is to use a coefficient related to total flow. Ralph Porges, for example, has estimated public and related water uses as 13.4 percent of total flow.

Residential water demand is the most important component and can be estimated using a method developed for HUD by Linnaweaver (reference below). This method makes fairly accurate estimates of water demand using a regression equation in which demand is related to income, size of plot, type of waste disposal, type of housing, whether the water is to be metered, and climate.

Alternatively, residential water demand can be estimated using the fairly conservative figure of 100 gallons per day per capita for single-family

EXHIBIT 6-4

HITTMAN ASSOCIATES WATER USAGE COEFFICIENTS

S.I.C. Number	Industrial Category	Mean Annual Usage Coefficient (gal/day/employee)
201	MEAT PRODUCTS	903.890
202	DAIRIES	791.350
203	CANNED, FROZEN FOODS	784.739
204	GRAIN MILLS	488.249
205	BAKERY PRODUCTS	220.608
206	SUGAR	1433.611
207	CANDY	244.306
208	BEVERAGES	1144.868
209	MISCELLANEOUS FOODS	1077.360
211	CIGARETTES	193.613
221	WEAVING, COTTON	171.434
222	WEAVING, SYNTHETICS	344.259
223	WEAVING, WOOL	464.439
225	KNITTING MILLS	273.439
226	TEXTILE FINISHING	810.741
227	FLOOR COVERING	297.392
228	YARN, THREAD MILLS	63.558
229	MISCELLANEOUS TEXTILES	346.976
230	WHOLE APPAREL INDUSTRY	20.000
242	SAW—PLANING MILL	223.822
243	MILLWORK	316.420
244	WOOD CONTAINERS	238.000
249	MISCELLANEOUS WOOD	144.745
251	HOME FURNITURE	122.178
259	FURNITURE FIXTURE	122.178
261	PULP MILLS	13,494.110
262	PAPER MILLS	2433.856
263	PAPERBOARD MILLS	2464.478
264	PAPER PRODUCTS	435.790
265	PAPERBOARD BOXES	154.804
266	BUILDING PAPER MILLS	583.355
270	WHOLE PRINT INDUSTRY	15.000
281	BASIC CHEMICALS	2744.401
282	FIBERS, PLASTICS	864.892
283	DRUGS	457.356
284	SOAP, TOILET GOODS	672.043
285	PAINT, ALLIED PRODUCTS	845.725
286	GUM—WOOD CHEMICALS	332.895
287	AGRICULTURE CHEMICALS	449.836
289	MISCELLANEOUS CHEMICALS	984.415
291	PETROLEUM REFINING	3141.100

Exhibit 6-4 (Continued)

HITTMAN ASSOCIATES WATER USAGE COEFFICIENTS

S.I.C. Number	Industrial Category	Mean Annual Usage Coefficient (gal/day/employee)
295	PAVING, ROOFING	829.592
301	TIRES, TUBES	375.211
302	RUBBER FOOTWEAR	82.592
303	RECLAIMED RUBBER	1031.523
306	RUBBER PRODUCTS	371.956
307	PLASTIC PRODUCTS	527.784
311	LEATHER TANNING	899.500
321	FLAT GLASS	590.140
322	PRESSED, BLOWN GLASSWARE	340.753
323	PRODUCTS OF PURCHASED GLASS	872.246
324	CEMENT, HYDRAULIC	279.469
325	STRUCTURAL CLAY	698.197
326	POTTERY PRODUCTS	326.975
327	CEMENT, PLASTER	353.787
328	CUT STONE PRODUCTS	534.789
329	NON-METALLIC MINERAL	439.561
331	STEEL-ROLLING	494.356
332	IRON, STEEL FOUNDRIES	411.052
333	PRIME NON-FERROUS	716.626
334	SECONDARY NON-FERROUS	1016.596
335	NON-FERROUS ROLLING	675.475
336	NON-FERROUS FOUNDRIES	969.586
339	PRIME METAL INDUSTRIES	498.331
341	METAL CANS	162.547
342	CUTLERY, HARDWARE	459.300
343	PLUMBING, HEATING	411.576
344	STRUCTURE, METAL	319.875
345	SCREW MACHINE	433.193
346	METAL STAMPING	463.209
347	METAL SERVICE	1806.611
348	FABRICATED WIRE	343.367
349	FABRICATED METAL	271.186
351	ENGINES, TURBINES	197.418
352	FARM MACHINERY	320.704
353	CONSTRUCTION EQUIPMENT	218.365
354	METALWORK, MACHINERY	196.255
355	SPECIAL INDUSTRY MACHINERY	290.494
356	GENERAL INDUSTRIAL MACHINERY	246.689
357	OFFICE MACHINES	138.025
358	SERVICE INDUSTRIAL MACHINE	334.203
359	MISCELLANEOUS MACHINES	238.839
361	ELECTRIC DISTRIBUTION PRODUCTS	272.001

EXHIBIT 6-4 (Continued)

HITTMAN ASSOCIATES WATER USAGE COEFFICIENTS

S.I.C. Number	Industrial Category	Mean Annual Usage Coefficient (gal/day/employee)
362	ELECTRIC INDUSTRIAL APPARATUS	336.016
363	HOME APPLIANCES	411.914
364	LIGHT-WIRING FIXTURES	369.592
365	RADIO-TV RECEIVING	235.763
366	COMMUNICATION EQUIPMENT	86.270
367	ELECTRONIC COMPONENTS	203.289
369	ELECTRIC PRODUCTS	393.272
371	MOTOR VEHICLES	318.233
372	AIRCRAFT AND PARTS	154.769
373	SHIP AND BOAT BUILDING	166.074
374	RAILROAD EQUIPMENT	238.798
375	MOTORCYCLE, BIKE	414.859
381	SCIENTIFIC INSTRUMENTS	181.007
382	MECHANICAL MEASURE	237.021
384	MEDICAL INSTRUMENTS	506.325
386	PHOTOGRAPHIC EQUIPMENT	120.253
387	WATCHES, CLOCKS	164.815
391	JEWELRY, SILVER	306.491
394	TOYS, SPORT GOODS	213.907
396	COSTUME JEWELRY	423.124
398	MISCELLANEOUS MANUFACTURING	258.270
399	MISCELLANEOUS MANUFACTURING	258.270

1. Maximum day and peak hour usage coefficients have not been determined at this time. Therefore, the library contains identical tables of the values as tabulated here for the mean annual usage coefficients.

Source: Hittman Associates, Inc., *Forecasting Municipal Water Requirements, Volume I.* Columbia, Md., 1969. NTIS No. PB 190275.

dwellings and 75 gallons per day per capita for apartments.

Compare the water demand for the proposed development to the existing supply and projected demands for water for the remainder of the community. Comment on whether or not water sources will be adequate for servicing this project. For ground water sources, compare demand figure to the safe yield previously reported. Do the same for all surface water sources. Will use of the water supply necessitate the construction of new water treatment, distribution, pumping, or supply facilities and if so, what would the cost of such construction be? Also, will the use of an aquifer or surface water resource affect water supply in other nearby or downstream communities?

Discuss any official plans to build facilities relating to water supply and how this relates to the short and long term impacts of the proposed project. Discuss any efforts to minimize water consumption.

For further information:

Hittman Associates, Inc., *Forecasting Municipal Water Requirements.* Columbia, Md., 1969. NTIS No. PB 190275.

Porges, Ralph, "Factors Influencing per Capital Water Consumption," *Water and Sewage Works*, Vol. 104, May 1957, pp. 199-204.

Linnaweaver, F. P., Jr., John C. Geyer, and Jerome B. Wolff, *A Study of Residential Water Use.* Study prepared for the Federal Housing Administration. Washington, D.C., U.S. Government Printing Office, 1967.

III.A.4.2. Sewerage

The impact of the environment with regard to sewerage on the proposed development is dependent on the type of sewage treatment which is contemplated. If private septic systems are to be used, the soil suitability for this purpose will have an impact on the design and cost of the systems. These should be discussed.

If public sewage disposal is to be used, whether or not sewage is to be treated at an existing or new facility is important. Public law 92-500 requires that all new public sewage treatment facilities have the capability for at least secondary sewage treatment and that all existing facilities be upgraded to this level by July 1, 1977. Thus, the cost of sewage treatment for the proposed development will vary according to whether sewage can be pumped to an existing secondary sewage treatment plant or a new plant must be built. The cost of additional pumping facilities and sewer lines must also be considered.

To investigate the impact of the proposed development on the environment, first project the amount of sewage that will be generated by the project. This is usually done by taking a percentage of the water demand. Alternative percentages are suggested by Linnaweaver (cited in section III.A.4.1.).

Next, discuss how the effluent will be treated. If septic systems are to be used, project any possible impacts of the systems on ground water quality. (See Dudley and Stephenson and Gordon, cited below.)

If public sewage treatment is to be used, note the level of treatment that will be employed. Based on the capacity of existing sewage treatment facilities, calculate the new facilities that will be needed. The water quality impact of both new and old facilities will then be based on the quantity of waste effluent and the level of treatment. Several models of the water quality impacts of sewage treatment facilities can be used to calculate the impacts (as given in Carey, *et al.*, cited below).

Discuss where the effluent from the proposed development will be treated and by whom. The latter is especially important, because the federal government will pay 75 percent of the cost of certain types of sewage treatment facilities.

For further information:

Carey, George W., *et al.*, *Urbanization, Water Pollution, And Public Policy*. New Brunswick, N.J., Rutgers University, Center for Urban Policy Research, 1972.

Dudley, John G. and David A. Stephenson, *Nutrient Enrichment of Ground Water from Septic Tank Disposal Systems*. Madison, Wis., Department of Geology for the Upper Great Lakes Regional Commission, 1973.

Gordon, Steven I., "Subsurface Movement of Septic Tank Wastes: Planning and Management Implications" in *Proceedings of the Water Resource Sessions, Middle States Division of the American Association of Geographers*. Syracuse, N.Y., Syracuse University, Department of Geography,

III.A.4.3. Solid Waste

Discuss any problems of solid waste disposal that might restrict the project's size. These might include short term restrictions on garbage truck capacity, the absence of a needed transfer station, or restrictions on the capacity of existing landfills. In each case, discuss whether these are temporary or long term in duration. Note whether the problem is local or statewide, and discuss mitigative action being contemplated by the developer.

Discuss the strategies and cost of solid waste treatment and their effect on housing costs.

Comment on local or state policies concerning solid waste and how this affects the project.

Calculate the impact of the proposed development on the solid waste system. Average per capita waste generation figures are available through EPA. Roy F. Weston has derived the following formula for per capita solid waste generation:

U=1.54 LogD — 0.68
V=U x 7 days/week x 1 ton/2000 lbs.
W=V x Population within given area
where: U=per capita waste generation in lbs./capita/day
D=Population density in persons per square mile
W=ton/week of waste generation within given area

This equation is valid in a poluation density range of 500-12,000 persons per square mile. For areas with less than 500 persons per square mile, the generation factor used is 3.4 pounds per capita per day. For those with more than 12,000 persons per square mile, the figure used is 5.6 pounds per capita per day.

These formulae provide some basis for calculating solid waste generation, although recent investigations by Greenberg (cited below) have brought the validity of this equation into question.

Based on the waste generation figures, describe the impact of the solid wastes on the area. These might include the effects of truck traffic hauling wastes and impacts on the capacity of transfer stations and final landfill or dump sites. Indicate whether the source of the impact is from residential, commercial, or industrial uses. Will there be short or long term effects? Will the proposed development influence appreciably the current way in which solid waste is being disposed?

For further information:

Greenberg, Michael R., Solid Waste Model for Northern New Jersey. Research in progress, 1974.

Weston, Roy F., Inc., *Macon County Solid Waste Management System Analysis*, Project No. 40.00 for State of Ill. Chicago, Illinois Institute for Environmental Quality, April 1974.

III.A.4.4. Drainage

Based on the description of the drainage infrastructure given above, discuss whether existing drainage capability will be able to service the proposed development. Note whether the drainage infrastructure will restrain future expansion of the project.

Comment on the costs of new drainage facilities and how they might affect total costs. Will drainage problems influence the project's residents and users? For example, frequent standing water or stagnant drainage systems might cause aesthetic or health problems. Drainage problems might also affect the use of recreation facilities, kill vegetation, disrupt septic systems, and damage foundations.

Discuss the impact of the proposed development on the local drainage capacity. Note the possibility, if any, of drainage overload. Discuss whether such problems will be short or long term, who will be affected, how severe the overload is expected to be, and whether actions will be taken or are contemplated by the developer to mitigate any adverse effects.

If new drainage facilities need to be installed, what will be the impact during the construction phase?

III.A.4.5. Energy

Discuss whether strained local energy resources will restrict the development's overall and individual unit size and the provision of such project amenities as air conditioning.

Comment on the impact of local utility prices on housing cost and operation. Note whether the prices of alternative energy resources have affected the design of the project or the types of energy sources that will be used. Will the future energy supplies in the region have any impact on the project?

Estimate the project's energy needs. This will vary according to the energy source and the heating and cooling efficiency of the building design. Data on average gas and electric consumption may be obtained from local utilities. Multiply the averages for each type of unit (for example, townhouse versus single-family dwellings) by the size and number of units in the development to obtain a total energy use estimate.

Evaluate whether existing energy sources will be adequate for servicing the project in light of the demand of the project, future demands for energy resources in the region as a whole, and future projected energy network capacity.

Discuss any efforts which have been made to conserve energy. For example, building design might include extra insulation or the building might be positioned to take full advantage of the microclimate. Also, discuss the location of the project in terms of the access by public and private transportation, location of places of employment of the residents, and what these might entail in terms of energy consumption for transportation.

Comment on how energy will be delivered to the site (for example, by overhead transmission lines, underground gas lines, or other means) and the impact this will have on the visual environment.

III.A.4.6. Transportation

Describe the accessibility of the site to employment, shopping centers, and other services. Discuss what affect this will have on the residents and users of the proposed developments.

Discuss whether mass transit facilities are available. The presence of such service may discourage automobile ownership and usage.

Note any efforts taken by the developer to encourage or discourage car use and travel, such as providing parking lots or prohibiting internal traffic in the project.

Describe any special design features which accomodate access to the site by mass transit, such as special bus turnaround areas.

Discuss the project's impact on existing transportation facilities. This analysis should include the following sections:

How many trips (more precisely, trip ends) will be generated by the proposed development? This will be a function of such factors as the income and other socioeconomic characteristics and the expected car ownership of the residents and users of the project.

What about the distribution of trips? Where will the trips originate and end? This will be influenced by such factors as the location and size of employment and shopping opportunities.

How many of the trips will be by automobile as opposed to mass transit? This bifurcation will be determined by such factors as car ownership, nature of the trip, and the availability and quality of mass transit facilities.

Precisely which routes will the trip take? Will this overload existing capacity? If so, how severely? What about future trips and transportation capacity? What will be the short versus long term effects of such overburden? What is being planned to minimize such harm, now and in the future? Are any efforts being made to discourage automobile usage?

For further information:

Donald A. Krueckeberg and Arthur L. Silvers, *Urban Planning Analysis Methods and Models*. New York, John Wiley, 1974.

III.A.5. AIR POLLUTION

Discuss the impacts of existing air pollution levels on the project's residents and users and on building maintenance costs. Describe any design features which have been incorporated into the plans in order to compensate for air pollution problems.

Discuss the impacts of the project on air pollution levels. These may be estimated using the traffic generation figures previously calculated, and information on the type of heating, cooling, and solid waste disposal systems for the project. Several models have been developed for projecting air pollution changes. (See references below.) Employ one of these models to project air pollution resulting from the project. Discuss any actions which will be taken to minimize these impacts. Note how increases in air pollution may affect health, flora and fauna, and other environmental conditions.

Compare projected air pollution levels with area standards and plans.

For further information:

Beals, Gordon A., *Guide to Local Diffusion of Air Pollutants*, Technical Report 214. Scott Air Force Base, Ill., U. S. Air Force, Air Weather Service, 1971.

Epstein, A. H., *et al.*, *A Guide for Considering Air Quality in Urban Planning*, Report prepared for U. S. Environmental Protection Agency. EPA-450/3-74-020. Springfield, Va., National Technical Information Service, 1974.

III.A.6. NOISE POLLUTION

Discuss the likely impact of existing noise levels on residents or users of the proposed project. Note the likely duration of present sound exposure.

Compare existing noise levels to official guidelines, such as HUD's "Noise Abatement and Control: Departmental Policy, Implementation Responsibilities and Standards." (Circular 1390.2.) To illustrate, external noise of 45 db(A) more than 30 minutes per 24 hours would be acceptable by HUD (for the purposes of granting either mortgage insurance or subsidies), while 80 db(A) for 60 minutes per 24 hours would generally be unacceptable. If existing noise exceeds guideline parameters, the project may be prohibited or may not receive federal mortgage insurance or subsidy.

Discuss strategies effected or proposed by the developer to reduce noise exposure to project residents. These might include screening with natural vegetation or extra sound insulation.

Describe to what degree the project will increase noise levels in the area during construction due to blasting, pile driving, machinery operation, and other activities. Compare the projected noise levels to the existing, ambient levels, and discuss the severity of the impact and how it relates to local noise control efforts and standards. Note the impact of the increased noise on adjacent land and on the fauna in the area.

Describe noise generated by the development after construction is completed. Sources of such noise might include heating and cooling systems, service vehicles, and increased traffic. Again, compare projected noise levels with existing, ambient levels and note the affect of the change on adjacent land uses and local fauna. How does this noise generation relate to local noise control efforts or standards?

Discuss any efforts being made to minimize the above impacts.

III.A.7. WATER POLLUTION

Describe whether local water quality will permit boating, swimming and other recreational uses. Note what impact this will have on both the residents and users of the proposed project.

Discuss any water pollution impacts not discussed under the section on sewage disposal (section III.A.4.2.). Include possible effects from urban storm runoff, sedimentation during and after construction, and from increases in local traffic. Describe impacts on the physical, chemical, and biological components of adjacent water bodies. Also, relate water quality changes to possible impacts on downstream water supplies and recreational areas. If new sewage treatment facilities must be built, will their presence have a secondary impact on development of adjacent areas?

Note the severity of the water quality impacts and whether the water quality degradation is within permissible levels for effluent, sewage discharge, and other factors. What actions are being taken to mitigate water quality impacts?

III.B. Social Environment
III.B.1. COMMUNITY FACILITIES

Comment on the availability and adequacy of local services such as garbage collection, schools, highway services, fire and police protection, social and health facilities, and recreation facilities. Note if municipal services will be supplemented by services provided by the developer.

Discuss the quality of local services, focusing on whether or not they are likely to be attractive to residents or users of the proposed project.

Discuss the cost of local services. If the latter is high, development may be opposed unless it generates sufficient revenues to offset local costs.

The proposed project will generally have two effects on local services:

a. The expansion of local services:
Precisely what will the municipality have to do to expand local services—for example, build new physical plant or hire new personnel?

b. The cost of local services:
How will the cost of servicing the project compare to the local revenue it will generate? Will the developer take any steps to reduce local use? Will the positive or negative local cost revenue impact be temporary or permanent?

The former section can be satisfied by talking to local officials in charge of the various services, as well as other responsible parties, such as town planners and local business administrators. The cost revenue analysis is more complicated and is examined below.

The overall cost revenue impact of a development can be projected by first calculating the school costs of an individual unit by multiplying the per-unit student multiplier by the local per-unit cost. (See exhibit 6-5.) Using household multipliers (given in exhibit 6-6), follow a similar approach for obtaining the nonschool cost per unit. Adding the educational and nonschool costs yields the total local cost per unit. The local revenue generated by the housing unit can be derived by multiplying the unit's valuation by the local "true" or equalized property tax rate. Substracting the total local cost from the local revenue yields the total unit surplus or deficit. To obtain the municipal cost-revenue impact of an *entire development* multiply the total *unit* surplus or deficit by the number of units in the development.

III.B.1.1. Schools

Describe the quality of existing local schools. This will be a determining factor in the satisfaction of project residents.

Comment on the local cost of schools. Note the trend of local educational expenditures, especially the school property tax.

EXHIBIT 6-5 PUBLIC SCHOOL ATTENDEES PER DWELLING UNIT BY NUMBER OF BEDROOMS

Bedroom Type	Grade Level	Pupil Multiplier
Garden Apartment		
One Bedroom	Kindergarten	.005
	Grammer School	.024
	High School	.017
		.046 (n = 1,816)
Two Bedroom	Kindergarten	.032
	Grammar School	.250
	High School	.062
		.344 (n = 1,072)
Townhouses		
Two Bedroom	Kindergarten	.029
	Grammar School	.134
	High School	.057
		.220 (n = 657)
Three Bedroom	Kindergarten	.097
	Grammar School	.450
	High School	.108
		.655 (n = 923)
Four Bedroom	Kindergarten	.125
	Grammar School	.712
	High School	.189
		1.026 (n = 109)
High Rise		
Studio	Kindergarten	.000
	Grammar School	.000
	High School	.000
		.000 (n = 158)
One Bedroom	Kindergarten	.006
	Grammar School	.006
	High School	.000
		.012 (n = 553)
Two Bedroom	Kindergarten	.021
	Grammar School	.115
	High School	.045
		.181 (n = 424)

EXHIBIT 6-5 PUBLIC SCHOOL ATTENDEES PER DWELLING UNIT BY NUMBER OF BEDROOMS (Continued)

Bedroom Type	Grade Level	Pupil Multiplier
Single Family[1]		
Three Bedroom	Kindergarten	.083
	Grammar School	.408
	High School	.135
		.626 (n = 362)
Four Bedroom	Kindergarten	.152
	Grammar School	.969
	High School	.172
		1.293 (n = 257)

1. Special Sample of Units < $30,000.

Source: George Sternlieb, *et al.*, *Housing Development and Municipal Costs*. New Brunswick, N.J., Rutgers University, Center for Urban Policy Research, 1973.

EXHIBIT 6-6

TOTAL HOUSEHOLD SIZE BY DWELLING TYPE
AND NUMBER OF BEDROOMS

Dwelling Type	Studio	1 Bedroom	2 Bedroom	3 Bedroom	4 Bedroom
Garden Apartments	—	1.902 (n = 1,816)	2.805 (n = 1,072)	—	—
Townhouses	—	—	2.675 (n = 657)	3.349 (n = 923)	3.741 (n = 109)
High Rise	1.151 (n = 158)	1.817 (n = 553)	2.484 (n = 424)	—	—
Single Family (under $30,000)	—	—	—	3.307 (n = 362)	3.720 (n = 257)

Source: George Sternlieb, *et al.*, *Housing Development and Municipal Costs*. New Brunswick, N.J., Rutgers University, Center for Urban Policy Research, 1973.

III.B.1.2. Health and Safety

Based on the description of the services provided for health, police and fire protection, and social services, describe how the quality of these services might affect the residents and users of the proposed development.

Pay particular attention to those services most likely to be used by project residents. For example, a residential development with a large number of elderly persons will require the availability of particular types of medical care.

Discuss the impact of the development on health, safety, and social services. Will additional medical facilities, physicians, police, and fire equipment and personnel be required to meet the needs generated by the development? How does the cost of these services relate to the taxes which the development will pay?

III.B.1.3. Recreation and Culture

Discuss how existing recreation facilities and cultural activities will affect the residents and users of the project. Describe the effects the project will have on these services and what additional needs might be generated by it.

Indicate any mitigating actions the developer will take to minimize the impacts on recreational and cultural activities. For example, the development may provide its own recreational space.

III.B.2. EMPLOYMENT

Discuss whether there are sufficient jobs in the area surrounding the proposed development to employ the projected residents.

Note whether the existing regional job requirements match the project residents' skills. If not, list any job training centers or programs that are available.

Describe whether regional jobs are located in close proximity to the proposed development or whether a long commute will be required.

Discuss the employment opportunities that will be generated by the development during construction.

Discuss whether the development will contain any commercial and other employment centers. Describe whether the latter will compete with existing firms. Estimate the number of jobs that will be generated directly and secondarily by the site and how this compares to existing employment levels.

Describe any efforts contemplated by the developer to attract employees to the site or area or to train project residents for existing jobs.

Discuss how this employment generation relates to official local and area-wide job planning.

III.B.3. SOCIOECONOMIC CHARACTERISTICS

Comment on whether the population of the nearby community will have any impact on the project. A small community may oppose a very large development.

Comment on how the development's projected racial structure compares to the community's racial breakdown. Community-development racial contrasts may lead to local opposition, but they also present an opportunity for racial integration.

Repeat the same for the other variables—age, education, occupation, imcome, and housing composition. Summarize how these socioeconomic characteristics will affect the project's residents and users.

Utilize the indices of social and economic conditions discussed in section II.B. of this outline to evaluate the extent and nature of the impacts of the area on the development and the development on the area.

Comment on the impact of the project on local population size. Compare the change to recent community population shifts.

Discuss whether the project will increase or decrease local racial mix.

Describe whether the development will change the local age distribution.

Comment on whether the project will increase or decrease average local income.

Repeat the same analysis with reference to other development and community characteristics, including educational attainment, occupation, housing composition, and other relevant variables.

Discuss the impact of the project on the relocation of any families, businesses, or industries now on or adjacent to the development site. Note any secondary relocation impacts resulting from the provision of roads or utility access routes.

III.B.4. OTHER IMPACTS—
OFFICIAL AND PRIVATE REACTION

Official and private reaction to a development may or may not reflect the actual impacts of a proposed project on the physical and social environment. However, it still remains important to comment on such reactions.

In this section describe the position of relevant public and private agencies and organizations regarding the proposed development. (See list below.) Discuss whether the project will conflict with public regulatory efforts, such as zoning, building and subdivision controls, or environmental or preservation actions. Among these may be a moratorium on building permits and other growth controls, preservation of open spaces on sites of archaeological, architectural, cultural, or historic value, or limits on the volume of traffic or sewerage.

If there is controversy surrounding the project, discuss the issues, the protagonists, and the intensity of the debate. Comment on likely future action. The evaluation-reaction of the following groups (where appropriate) should be described.

Federal government:
    HUD
    Other federal agencies, such as the Departments of Transportation
    and Labor.

State government:
　State elected officials
　State environmental protection agencies
　State departments of community affairs or housing
　Other state agencies, dealing with landmarks preservation, traffic
　utilities, building codes, and other relevant activities

Local government:
　Town council, assembly or other legislative body
　Other elected officials
　Local planning board
　Local environmental protection agency
　Other local agencies, such as the department of traffic

Other governmental bodies:
　County planning board
　Council of government
　Other agencies

Judiciary:
　Existing or pending litigation

Private Organizations
　Lobbying or special interest groups
　Local citizen groups
　Other groups either supporting or attacking the project or likely to do so

III.C. Aesthetic Environment

Describe whether existing regional general aesthetic features will favorably affect the expected residents or users of the proposed project.

Discuss whether development style, size, or landscaping will harmonize with existing architectural styles and protect natural features.

Comment on efforts that will be taken both during and after construction to preserve or enhance historic and archeological sites, architecturally significant properties, and other aesthetic features.

Using the checklist provided in the previous discussion on aesthetics (exhibit 6-4), note any alterations of the environment that might have an impact on scenic resources.

Comment on whether the development can potentially destory or obstruct the view of existing special natural features. Discuss efforts to avoid or minimize such action.

Discuss whether the project will destroy or harm historic and archaeological sites or scenic areas (either during or after construction).

In the above discussions, note the severity of the project's impact, the duration of any change, and its relationship to local or regional preservation efforts.

For further information:

Boaz, Joseph N., ed., *Architectural Graphic Standards.* New York, John Wiley, 1970.

Lynch, Kevin, *Site Planning.* Boston, MIT Press, 1965.

Proshansky, Harold M., *et al.*, eds., *Environmental Psychology: Man and His Physical Setting.* New York, Holt, Rhinehart, Winston, 1970.

Redding, Martin J., *Aesthetics in Environmental Planning.* Washington, D.C., U.S. Government Printing Office, 1973. Available through NTIS, No. PB-229-574.

IV. INTERNAL PROJECT ENVIRONMENT

Large developments (such as urban renewal efforts, large multi-family housing projects, new communities or subdivisions) create their own *internal* environments that can add to or detract from the quality of life they produce. Quality of life is rather difficult to measure; people's opinions vary widely on what constitutes a high quality environment. However, certain information is available on how large projects may affect the internal physical, social, and aesthetic environment.

IV.A. Physical Environment
Discuss the internal physical environment of the project. What special design features have been used to enhance the security of the grounds and dwellings? Have any special provisions been made to allow access to the site and safe movement through the site by bicyclists and pedestrians? Describe the proposed design and site plan and how it might affect noise levels, air pollution, and physical access to buildings and other facilities.

IV.B. Social Environment
Discuss the internal social environment. Are any provisions being made for meeting places or other social activities? Will racial and social integration be encouraged? How? Will the design provide for adequate privacy? What types of recreational and cultural activities will be provided or encouraged?

IV.C. Aesthetic Environment
Finally, describe the internal aesthetic environment. What measures will the developer take to effect a pleasant aesthetic environment? Include a description of physical building appearance, landscaping, and other design.

V. ALTERNATIVES TO THE PROPOSED ACTION

As numerous courts have interpreted the NEPA requirements, and as a recent HUD report emphasized, it is important to consider all competing alternatives to a proposed project in order to examine whether the planned development is the best among competing alternatives. (See David Mudarri, *Environmental Assessments for Project Level Actions.* HUD Office of Environmental Quality, 1974.) In order to do this it is important to carefully consider all competing alternatives to the proposal. The alternatives examined should include those which serve the same general objective as the proposed development but a null strategy (no project) should be considered.

The discussion in this section should focus on listing what alternatives were considered and examining why they were rejected. It should include the following sections:

a. Evaluate whether the project is really necessary. What needs does it satisfy? What would be the social or physical environmental consequences if the project were not built? Which groups, areas would be affected? Differentiate short and long term consequences.

b. Indicate alternative sites owned, controlled, or potentially available which would be investigated if the recommended site is unacceptable. What are the advantages and disadvantages of building on the alternative locations?

c. Discuss alternatives which were considered in terms of project.
   1. Size—anticipated resident or user population or density.
   2. Design—number and height of buildings and placement on site, architectural and design treatment, and land uses.

d. What additional alternatives, or modification to the proposed site or design, could be investigated to reduce adverse environmental impacts?

VI. UNAVOIDABLE ADVERSE ENVIRONMENTAL EFFECTS

Some impacts can be entirely avoided by not effecting the proposed action, others may be ameliorated by implementing modifications and changes, while still others cannot be addressed through any course of action. There are also trade-offs in trying to reduce certain impacts because such actions may aggravate other effects. Unavoidable adverse environmental effects must be listed, but this analysis should be kept in perspective by noting mitigative actions. The discussion in this section should include the following considerations:

VI.A. Unavoidable Adverse Physical Impacts
Review the adverse physical effects resulting from the proposed development. Reference previous sections as appropriate. Discuss the alternatives in design which were considered, their adverse physical effects, and the final, selected design and its environmental effects.

VI.B. Unavoidable Adverse Social Impacts
Review the adverse social effects resulting from the development with reference to previous sections. What trade-offs had to be made among

adverse physical and social impacts and the possible benefits of the project?

VI.C. Unavoidable Adverse Aesthetic Impact

Summarize the adverse aesthetic impacts which may result from the proposed development. Describe efforts which were made to minimize these effects and those impacts which could not be avoided.

VI.D. Mitigative Actions by the Developer, Government, or Private Groups

In this section summarize actions described in section III taken or being contemplated by the developer, governmental agencies, and others to enhance environmental quality and reduce adverse environmental impacts. Note whether such activities are firmly underway or are only tentative or preliminary. It would be useful to organize this section in terms of actions by the developer, by government, and by private groups.

VI.D.1. ACTIONS BY THE DEVELOPER

Discuss and describe the following:

a. *Reports and studies commissioned.* What information has the developer gathered on the existing site and area environment and the likely impact of his project? Whom has be contacted? What reports have been written? Is the developer following the recommendations of these reports?

b. *Measures taken during construction.* What activities or strategies is the developer following during construction in order to minimize environmental degradation; for example, scheduling building at night or protecting existing trees, and ground cover?

c. *Measures taken after construction.* What strategies are being followed after construction to preserve the environment? Be specific. Describe all activities and project modification, such as measures to reduce air pollution levels or excessive noise levels (air conditioning, noise barriers, setbacks or greenbelts, or insulation); erosion and siltation control measures; drainage systems; on-site sewerage or solid waste disposal facilities or expansion of local or regional systems; landscaping and preservation of natural areas or green space; landscaping and preservation of cover; screening; expansion of community facilities; discussion of impact with community groups; special architectural treatment; and preservation or relocation of historic property.

d. *Rejected measures.* Describe preservatory measures that were considered but rejected. Discuss the reasons for such rejection.

VI.D.2. ACTIONS BY GOVERNMENT

Discuss and describe the following:

a. *Governmental studies.* What studies or reports have been done or commissioned by governmental agencies to assess the environmental quality of the existing project site and area, and the likely impact of the project?

b. *New or expanded infrastructures.* What measures are being taken or contemplated by governmental agencies to create or expand infrastructure and community facilities and services to meet the demand imposed by the project and by growth in the area? These might include new or expanded sewerage and sewage treatment plants, mass transit systems, or similar measures.

c. *New or expanded controls.* Are federal, state, or local governmental bodies contemplating new or expanded controls to protect the environment? These might include controls imposed by appropriate agencies or governmental bodies to preserve natural areas, open space or historic sites; plans to anticipate and cope with the long term impact of the project specifically and growth in the area in general; or efforts to reduce pollution levels in the area.

VI.D.3. ACTIONS BY PRIVATE GROUPS

Discuss and describe actions taken to mitigate the project's impact on the environment, including:

a. *Reports and studies.* Describe any reports done or commissioned by private groups to examine the environmental impact of the project.

b. *Preservation efforts.* Discuss any private actions to enhance environmental quality or reduce adverse environmental impacts of the projects, such as buying land or buildings for preservation.

c. *Other efforts.* Briefly discuss other private efforts, such as lobbying or litigation, to enhance environmental quality.

VI.E. Alternatives' Adverse Environmental Impact

Discuss environmental impacts of the project which would have been avoided by the adoption of one of the alternative strategies (discussed in section V).

Comment on the environmental impacts of the project which could not be avoided by any alternative.

Review environmental impacts of alternative strategies which were avoided by choosing the proposed action.

VII. IMPACTS OVER TIME

It is important in discussing environmental impacts to identify the period over which impacts might occur. Certain impacts may occur only during the construction phase of a project. Other impacts may immediately follow construction but will not extend for too long afterwards. Finally, impacts may involve changes to the environment or commitments of resources that will extend long into the future. These three periods of impact should be discussed separately as outlined below.

VII.A. Construction Phase

Impacts which will occur during the construction phase of the project should be listed. These include such things as impacts on local traffic due to construction, dust, short term erosion and sedimentation, noises from construction activities and equipment, and relocation. Reference should be made to discussion of specific impacts in other sections. A list of construction activities and equipment, hours of use, and expected duration of each phase of construction would help to illustrate this section.

VII.B. Short Term Impacts

Short term impacts are those project effects that will extend beyond the construction phase but for only a short period of time. For example, erosion will continue to occur after construction is completed until vegetation has grown enough to hold the soil in place, often resulting in short term impacts on water quality.

List and discuss briefly the short term impacts of the proposed project and measures to alleviate them.

VII.C. Long Term Impacts

Long term impacts are those which will last long after the project is completed, such as increased demand for public services, unavoidable pollution impacts, and irreversible commitments of resources. The desirability of completing the project now should be compared with the long term options which will be eliminated because of the development.

Discuss these impacts with reference to previous sections of the statement.

VIII. IRREVERSIBLE AND IRRETRIEVABLE COMMITMENTS OF RESOURCES LIKELY TO RESULT FROM IMPLEMENTATION OF THE PROPOSED PROJECT

Discuss irreversible and irretrievable commitments. An effect is irreversible and a resource is irretrievable if, once development is effected, the impacts cannot be obviated by any available countermeasure. To illustrate, construction that would destroy prime agriculture land would constitute an irretrievable commitment of resources. The construction of an extensive infrastructure to support a project is for all practical purposes an irreversible commitment, since large commitments of resources make removal or abandonment thereafter improbable.

Discuss the magnitude of the resource commitment. Note also primary and secondary impacts. To illustrate development may not immediately destroy agricultural land (previously cited as an example of an irretrievable resource utilization), but it may spur secondary development that has the same effect.

Care should be taken in this section not to merely repeat impacts discussed in previous sections. The focus here is on *resource* utilization rather than just impact on the *environment*. Many EIS documents ignore this distinction and merely repeat environmental impacts which more appropriately belong in sections III. (Impact on the Environment) and VI. (Unavoidable Adverse Environmental Impacts).

For further information:

Hopkins, Lewis D., *Environmental Impact Statements: A Handbook for Writers and Reviewers*. Urbana, University of Illinois, Illinois Institute for Environmental Quality, 1973.

Major problems faced by anyone who must prepare or review an EIS are knowing where to turn for additional information and, once these sources are located, how to understand the material presented. This section attempts to rectify this shortcoming by listing EIS resources.

Part One lists useful EIS *published materials*. Official EIS guidelines and other sources of guidance, as well as the addresses of these information sources, are presented first. Next an extensive EIS literature, including books, periodicals, and other sources, is reviewed and annotated. This is followed by a comprehensive listing of abstracts and indices useful for the EIS writer or reviewer.

Part Two lists *public and private organizations* that can be contacted for aid in EIS preparation or review. It first focuses on general professional groups, and then specific public, professional, and academic organizations. It then gives examples of information sources for various EIS substantive sections.

Part Three is a *glossary* of common environmental terms often found in the EIS literature.

PART I: PUBLISHED MATERIALS

EIS Guidelines Available at State, County, and Local Levels

1. ARIZONA: EIS guidelines are required for all water oriented development projects. Guidelines are available from the Arizona Game and Fish Department.

    Contact: Chief
Wildlife Planning and Development Division
Arizona Game and Fish Department
2222 West Greenway Road

Phoenix, Arizona 85023
Telephone: (602) 942-3000

2. CALIFORNIA: "Guidelines for implementation of the California Environmental Quality Act of 1970" currently available as amended 12/17/73.

Contact: Secretary
California Resources Agency
Room 1311
1416 Ninth Street
Sacramento, California 95814
Telephone: (916) 445-9134

A) Marin County: Revised procedures and guidelines are available in checklist format.

Contact: Environmental Coordinator
Department of Environmental Coordination
Marin County Civic Center
San Raphael, California 94903
Telephone: (415) 479-1100

B) Sacramento   Guidelines and procedures are available for the
   County: county to implement the California Environmental Quality Act of 1970 as amended.

Contact: Environmental Coordinator
Environmental Impact Section
Sacramento County Community Development
    and Environmental Protection Agency
827 7th Street, Room 327
Sacramento, California 95814

3. COLORADO: Guidelines for EIS compliance with amendment Chapter 106 (Colorado Revised Statutes, 1963) are available.

Contact: Director
Division of Planning
Department of Local Affairs
Room 524
1575 Sherman Street

Denver, Colorado 80203
Telephone: (303) 892-2128

A) City of   Guidelines are available for preparation of
   Lakewood: environmental impact statements for all land uses.
                      Currently applicable to all rezonings (including
                      PUD's) and public works projects (where the city
                      is the developer) and selected areas of building
                      permits.

Contact: Environmental Control Officer
                      Department of Community Development
                      1580 Yarrow Street
                      Lakewood, Colorado 80215
                      Telephone: (303) 232-0212

4. CONNECTICUT: Guidelines are currently being prepared to implement
                      EIS under Connecticut Environmental Policy Act
                      (Public Act 73-562)

Contact: Director of Planning and Research
                      Department of Environmental Protection
                      State Office Building
                      Hartford, Connecticut
                      Telephone: (203) 566-4202

5. DELAWARE: Environmental Impact Statements required for all
                      industrial projects in the Coastal Zone, as required by
                      Coastal Zone Act (Title 7, Chapter 70, Delaware
                      Code). Guidelines are found within the statute.

Contact: Chief
                      Coastal Zone Management
                      Delaware State Planning Office
                      530 S. duPont Highway
                      Dover, Delaware 19901
                      Telephone: (302) 678-4271

                      Additionally, the Wetlands Law (Title 7 Chapter 66,
                      Delaware Code) under the Department of Natural
                      Resources and Environmental Control requires an
                      environmental impact statement. Guidelines currently
                      in draft form.

Contact:	Department of Natural Resources and Environmental Control Dover, Delaware Telephone: (302) 678-4403

6. FLORIDA: Guidelines for the implementation of Environmental Control Law Chapters 253 and 403 and the Water Management Act of 1972, Chapter 380, Florida Statutes, are available in the form of administrative rules and regulations.

Contact: Director of Environmental
Protection Section
Florida Game and Freshwater Fish Commission
Bryant Building
Tallahassee, Florida 32304
Telephone (904) 488-6661

7. HAWAII: Guidelines currently being prepared to implement EIS under Act, 246 Sesion Laws of Hawaii, Chapter 343.

Contact: Director
Office of Environmental Quality Control
Office of the Governor
550 Halekaowila Street
Room 301
Honolulu, Hawaii 96813
Telephone: (808) 548-6915

8. MAINE: Comprehensive guidelines and instructions are available for the completion of the environmental impact statement in accordance with the laws administered by the Bureau of Land Quality Control with referral to review agencies appropriate to the specific project.

Contact.   State of Maine
State House
Department of Environmental Protection
Augusta, Maine 04330

or

Director
State Planning Office

189 State Street
Augusta, Maine
Telephone: (207) 289-3261

9. MARYLAND:

Guidelines are available to aid state agencies to comply with Section 451 of the Maryland Environmental Policy Act. They emanate from the Department of Natural Resources.

Contact:

Maryland Department of Natural Resources
Annapolis, Maryland
Telephone: (301) 267-5548

10. MASSACHUSETTS:

Regulations and guidelines pursuant to General Laws, Chapter 30, Section 62 relating to the Preparation of Environmental Impact Reports, for state projects, are available.

Contact:

Secretary of Environmental Affairs
Executive Office of Environmental Affairs
18 Tremont Street
Boston, Massachusetts 02108
Telephone: (617) 727-7700

A) Brookline:

Guidelines available in accordance with Section 5.09 Environmental Impact and Design Review procedures adopted December 10, 1973.

Contact:

Town Clerk's Office
333 Washington Street
P.O. Box 1000
Brookline, Massachusetts 02147

11. MINNESOTA:

Guidelines are available for compliance with the Minnesota Environmental Policy Act of 1973 which requires an EIS for both state and private activities.

Contact:

Director for Environmental Planning
State Planning Agency
Capitol Square Building
550 Cedar Street—Room 100

St. Paul, Minnesota 55101
Telephone: (612) 296-3985

12. MISSISSIPPI: Currently an EIS is required only under
                         Mississippi Coastal Wetlands Protection Act,
                         Chapter 385, Laws of 1973. Guidelines for
                         compliance are available.

   Contact: Director
                         Mississippi Marine Resources Council
                         P.O. Box 497
                         Long Beach, Mississippi 39560
                         Telephone: (601) 864-4602

13. MONTANA: Guidelines for EIS in compliance with Montana
                         Environmental Policy Act are available; they are
                         also included as an Appendix to the
                         Environmental Quality Council's Annual Report.

   Contact: Executive Director
                         Environmental Quality Council
                         Capital Station
                         Helena, Montana 59601
                         Telephone: (406) 449-3742

14. NEVADA: Guidelines are available for the compliance with
                         the Nevada Clean Air Act, Chapter 445, Nevada
                         Revised Statutes.

   Contact: Chief
                         Bureau of Environmental Health
                         Commission of Environmental Protection
                         1209 Johnson Street
                         Carson City, Nevada 89701
                         Telephone: (702) 885-4670

15. NEW JERSEY: Guidelines are available for all projects falling
                         within the purview of the "Coastal Area Review
                         Act," Executive Order No. 53 (State funded
                         projects in excess of $1 million not reviewed at
                         the federal level), as well as those private projects
                         which may be requested to submit an EIS.

   Contact: Chief
                         Office of Environmental Review
                         Department of Environmental Protection

John Fitch Plaza, P.O. Box 1390
Trenton, New Jersey 08625
Telephone: (609) 292-2662

16. NEW YORK: Guidelines are available in the form of a simple
                         check off on pre-printed form (similar to A-95).

Contact: Director of Environmental Analysis
                         Department of Environmental Conservation
                         Albany, New York 12201
                         Telephone: (518) 457-2223

A) Suffolk   A comprehensive set of guidelines are
   County: available to assist county departments in
                         compliance with policies set by the county
                         executive.

Contact: Council on Environmental Quality
                         County of Suffolk
                         H. Lee Dennison Building
                         County Center
                         Hauppauge, New York 11787
                         Telephone: (516) 979-2798

B) Town of   A general application/guidelines format is
   Huntington: available for all applicants for a change of
                         zone, subdivision, site improvement,
                         building permit or a license to occupy or use
                         property in the Town of Huntington.

C) Town of   Guidelines are available in checklist format
   Penfield: for both long and short form EIS
                         requirements.

Contact: Director of Public Works
                              Penfield, New York
                              Telephone: (716) 377-5500

17. NORTH CAROLINA: Guidelines available for compliance with EIS
                    requirement applicable to state funded projects.

Contact: Assistant Secretary for Resource Management
                              Department of Natural and Economic Resources
                              P.O. Box 27687
                              Raleigh, North Carolina 27611
                              Telephone: (919) 829-4984

18. RHODE ISLAND: A complete summary of natural resource laws and
                    environmental coverage is available.

Contact: Statewide Planning
                              Department of Administration
                              265 Melrose Street
                              Providence, Rhode Island 02907
                              Telephone: (401) 277-2656

19. TEXAS: Guidelines are available for compliance with
                    suggested policy of the Interagency Council on
                    Natural Resources and Environment; although
                    filing of an impact statement is not required by
                    state law, all member agencies are encouraged to
                    cooperate in the environmental effort.

Contact: Director, Division of Planning Coordination
                              Office of the Governor
                              P.O. Box 12428
                              Austin, Texas 78711
                              Telephone: (512) 475-2427

20. UTAH: Brief guidelines are available in outline form
                    describing the content of an environmental
                    impact statement, required by the Executive
                    Order on Environmental Quality (state agencies).

Contact.   State Planning Coordinator
                              State of Utah
                              118 Capital Building
                              Salt Lake City, Utah 84111
                              Telephone: (801) 328-5245

21. VERMONT:

Regulations and criteria pertaining to the Vermont Land Use and Development Law are available. This is not a step by step procedural guideline for filing an environmental impact statement; it is rather a broad outline of applicability.

Contact:

Assistant Secretary
Agency of Environmental Conservation
Montpelier, Vermont 05602
Telephone: (802) 828-3309

22. VIRGINIA:

Currently a publication is available detailing who must file an EIS (state agencies in the executive branch engaged in projects costing in excess of $100,000); procedural guidelines are appended to this report.

Contact:

Environmental Impact Coordinator
Council on the Environment
Room 1103
8th Street Office Building
Richmond, Virginia 23219
Telephone: (804) 770-4500

23. WASHINGTON:

Official guidelines are currently being promulgated and will supercede the interim guidelines of December 1972.

Contact:

Office of Planning and Program Development
Department of Ecology
Olympia, Washington 98504
Telephone: (206) 753-6890

24. WISCONSIN:

Comprehensive guidelines for compliance with both Chapter 274, Laws of 1971 (WEPA) are available, including a sample worksheet as well as criteria for filing, as per Executive Order No. 69.

Contact:

Secretary
Department of Natural Resources
Box 450
Madison, Wisconsin 53701
Telephone: (608) 266-2121

EIS Literature: Selected Annotated Bibliography

BOOKS

Ashmun, Candace M. and Peter W. Larson, MUNICIPAL LAND USE DECISIONS, THE TOOLS AND THE METHODS, To be published cooperatively by the Bedminister Township (N.J.) and the Upper Raritan Watershed Association (N.J.).

This manual forcuses on attempting to clarify the role of environmental assessment in the municipal decision-making process. It is designed to explain why such an assessment is vital and the techniques of evaluation used in planning and land use. The manual is written in an effort to justify the time, simplify the process, and clarify the impact procedures so that they can be effectively used and properly administered.

Carter, Steven; Frost, Murray; Rubin, Claire; Sumek, Lyle, ENVIRONMENTAL MANAGEMENT AND LOCAL GOVERNMENT, Office of Research and Development, U.S. Environmental Protection Agency, Washington, D.C.: February 1974, 389 pp.

This report presents the results of a study of environmental management at the local government level. The study has two main components: a survey of chief executives in cities over 10,000 population and counties over 50,000; and, a series of field studies of local environmental management in Dallas, Texas; Inglewood, California; Miamisburg, Ohio; and the Piedmont Triad Region, North Carolina. Discussions center around capacity for handling EIS locally. If EIS is already ongoing, structure for its completion is discussed.

Citizens Advisory Committee on Environmental Quality, ANNUAL REPORT TO THE PRESIDENT AND TO THE COUNCIL ON ENVIRONMENTAL QUALITY FOR THE YEAR ENDING MAY 1972, Washington, D.C., Government Printing Office: no date.

This report evaluates urbanization as an important determinant of environmental quality. It notes the importance that local governmental bodies have on the urbanization process and discusses their role in regulating the environment.

Council on Environmental Quality, ENVIRONMENTAL QUALITY ANNUAL REPORT (3RD) OF THE COUNCIL ON ENVIRONMENTAL QUALITY, August 1972, 475 pp.

The report emphasizes both status of and trends in environmental quality. It discusses the interrelationships of population, technology, pollution and other factors that will shape our future environment. It covers recent EIS developments at the federal, state, and local levels.

Dickert, Thomas G.; Domeny, Katherine R. (eds), ENVIRONMENTAL IMPACT ASSESSMENT: GUIDELINES AND COMMENTARY, University of California, Berkeley, California: 1974, 238 pp.

This volume covers a broad spectrum of issues relating to the environments. These include the relationship of EIS to local and state planning processes, methods of environmental impact assessment, social, economic and legal interpretations of matters relating to NEPA and California Environmental Quality Act. An excellent and current source volume.

Enk, Gordon A., BEYOND NEPA—CRITERIA FOR ENVIRONMENTAL IMPACT REVIEW, The Institute on Man and Science, Rensselaerville, New York: May 1973, 140 pp.

An examination of the responses of state and federal agencies to the mandate of the National Environmental Policy Act of 1969. It reviews the procedures of each of the states with respect to EIS as well as an in-depth look at those states with laws comparable to NEPA.

Hemenway, Gail D., DEVELOPER'S HANDBOOK—ENVIRONMENTAL IMPACT STATEMENTS, Associated Home Builders of the Greater East Bay Inc., Berkeley, California: 1973, 60 pp.

This document explores the significance of the environmental impact statement in the life of the private developer with reference to when should it be prepared, what should it include, and who should prepare it. These topics are examined through the aid of a hypothetical case. It additionally includes much in the way of relevant and supporting related material and references.

Hopkins, Lewis D., ENVIRONMENTAL IMPACT STATEMENTS: A HANDBOOK FOR WRITERS AND REVIEWERS, Illinois Institute for Environmental Quality, Chicago, Ill.: Aug. 1974, 207 pp.

The report is directed at impact statements for capital facilities which are the concern of state, rather than local or federal officials, e.g. resevoirs, stream channelization, highway links, mining operations, and public facility location.

Joint Committtee on Continuing Legal Education of the American Law Institute and the American Bar Association, ENVIRONMENTAL LAW — IV STUDY MATERIALS, Philadelphia, Pa.: 1974, 323 pp.

This document consists of a series of papers presented at the ALI — ABA Course of Study, Environmental Law — IV in San Francisco, February 7-9, 1974. It covers a wide spectrum of legal/procedural issues relating to EIS. A concise summary of "little" NEPA laws is included.

Ortolano, L.; Hill, W.W., AN ANALYSIS OF ENVIRONMENTAL STATEMENTS FOR CORPS OF ENGINEERS WATER PROJECTS, Stanford University, Department of Civil Engineering, Stanford, Calif.: 1972, 146 pp.

This book discusses the results of an intensive analysis of 234 Corps of Engineers environmental impact statements prepared in accordance with Sec. 102 (2) (C) of NEPA. The proper role of environmental impact statements is suggested and an assessment and suggestions for improvement of the 234 statements is rendered. While many of the reports analyzed are foreign to housing, the comments are pointed and well taken for impact statements related to housing.

Ortolano, Leonard, (ed.), ANALYZING THE ENVIRONMENTAL IMPACTS OF WATER PROJECTS, Stanford University, Department of Civil Engineering, Stanford, Calif.: March 1973, 433 pp.

This is a report of a year-long interdisciplinary seminar conducted at Stanford University. It was aimed at developing and testing a structured, systematic methodology for the identification, description, measurement, and display of environmental impacts associated with water resources development activity. It concludes that, rather than a "cookbook" approach, a conceptual framework which defines and relates major factors and terms relevant to environmental impact assessment together with a general analytical orientation is needed.

University of Pennsylvania Center for Ecological Research in Planning and Design, MEDFORD PERFORMANCE REQUIREMENTS FOR THE MAINTENANCE OF SOCIAL VALUES REPRESENTED BY THE NATURAL ENVIRONMENT OF MEDFORD TOWNSHIP, N.J., Center for Ecological Research in Planning and Design, University of Pennsylvania, Philadelphia, Pa.: 1974, 64 pp.

This report is one of the most innovative efforts to replace traditional planning and zoning by an ecologically focused approach. It attempts to identify areas which were propitious for prospective types of land uses employing explicit criteria and method. The report proposes appropriate performance specifications to help achieve this objective.

PERIODICALS

Ackerman, Bruce L., "Impact Statements and Low Cost Housing," SOUTHERN CALIFORNIA LAW REVIEW Vol. 46, June 1973, pp. 754+.

This article outlines the problems created by the National Environmental Policy Act and the California Environmental Quality Act for low-income and working class families who are seeking decent housing. The effects of delay upon the construction of low cost subsidized housing are often undesirable. In addition the article offers some proposals for reconciling the sometimes competing interests of environmentalists and people in need of housing.

Administrative Law—Judicial Review, "Agency Threshold Decision Not to Prepare NEPA Environmental Impact Statement Subject to Judicial Review Under Standard of Reasonableness. *Save Our Ten Acres v. Kreger*," 472 F.2d 463 (5th Cir. 1973) GEORGIA LAW REVIEW, Vol. 7, 1973, pp. 785+.

The court in this case faced the issue of whether the court could review an agency's threshold decision that the project in question would have no significant impact, and determined that such a review was in order. The article considers the merits of this action and makes recommendations to clarify necessary considerations for a threshold decision. The "threshold" decision is of growing importance in EIS; increased clarity in this area is essential.

Anderson, Frederick R., "The National Environmental Policy Act: How It Is Working, How It Should Work," THE ENVIRONMENTAL LAW REPORTER, Environmental Law Institute, January 1974, 4 pp.

This paper discusses certain changes in the implementation of the National Environmental Policy of 1969 which could make the act go much further toward the realization of its innovative mandate. It deals largely with ways to overcome some of the bureaucratic resistance the act has thus far encountered. Its specific relation to EIS is a description of the processing and potential delays of an EIS filing.

Andrews, Richard N.L., "A Philosophy of Environmental Impact Assessment," JOURNAL OF SOIL AND WATER CONSERVATION, September-October 1973, pp. 197+.

This article discusses the NEPA requirements and reviews different frameworks of environmental impact assessment.

Bisaccio, Gary A. "Goose Hollow Foothills League v. Romney—When Is An Environmental Impact Statement Required?" ENVIRONMENTAL LAW, Vol. 2, 1972, pp. 412+.

The case detailed in this article presents a guide to when it is necessary to file an environmental impact statement related to housing. The particular case involves the construction of a sixteen story high rise apartment building for which the Department of Housing and Urban Development had provided funds.

Clark, Robert A., "A Time of Uncertainty—Developers Struggle To Meet Environmental Demands," THE MORTGAGE BANKER, August 1973, pp. 10+.

The article views the environmentalist—developer dichotomy as one that is to some extent exaggerated but nevertheless a real problem which must be overcome for the sake of both factions. It reviews some of the causes of the problems and articulates potential resolutions to this dilemma. The developers' plight in EIS is articulately presented.

Council on Environmental Quality, 102 MONITOR. Executive Office Of The President, Washington, D.C.

The 102 Monitor is the monthly publication of the Council on Environmental Quality. In addition to its listing of environmental impact statements which have been filed under the provisions of section 309 of the Clean Air Act, as amended; items of current concern in NEPA case law; and information on the environmental studies of the council. Copies are distributed monthly to state governments and government documents sections of major libraries.

D'Amato, Anthony; Baxter, James, "The Impact of Impact Statements Upon Agency Responsibility: A Prescriptive Analysis," IONA LAW REVIEW, Vol. 59, December 1973, pp. 195+.

The purpose of this article is to explore a federal agency's duties with respect to NEPA once the decision to prepare an impact statement has been made. It describes what an agency must consider for a full and fair reading of NEPA, while attempting to present a workable system of legal prescriptions for agency compliance with both the letter and spirit of NEPA. One gains a clear perspective of the developing review criteria associated with EIS processing.

Durchslag, Melvyn R. and Junger, Peter D., "HUD and the Human Environment: A Preliminary Analysis Of The National Environmental Policy Act of 1969 Upon The Department of Housing and Urban Development," IOWA LAW REVIEW, Vol. 58, 1973, pp. 805+.

This article examines the effect of environmental policy upon the urban environment with specific attention to the provisions of NEPA. It discusses the potential ramifications of Sec. 102 (2) (C) as applicable to urban environments and as a means of dealing with the problems encountered there. The conflicts of immediate housing for the poor versus declining neighborhood environment as a function of increased development are underscored.

"Environmental Control: Environmental Impact Statements Must Include Discussion of Alternatives Beyond Scope of Authority of Reporting Body," MINNESOTA LAW REVIEW, Vol. 57, 1973, pp. 632+.

This comment discusses the implications of the court's decision in Natural Resources Defense Council v. Morton, 458 F. 2d 827 (D.C. Cir. 1972). This is the source of the oft-repeated statement that an impact statement not only must evaluate a proposed action in terms of environmental impact, but must also be viewed as a full *disclosure law with respect to the necessary discussion of alternatives to the proposed action.*

"Environmental Law: The Mini-Impact Statement Requirement," WASHBORN LAW JOURNAL, Vol. 13, 1974, pp. 140+.

This article comments on the Hanly v. Kleindienst case, 471 F. 2d 823 (2d Cir. 1972) with respect to whether or not an impact statement was necessary for the construction of a twelve story federal jail in downtown Manhattan. It deals more than any article with the issues and substantive content which surround discussion of the human environment in EIS.

"Environmental Law — Rucker Willis: Are Impact Statements for Private Projects That Require Federal Permits an Endangered Species," NORTH CAROLINA LAW REVIEW, Vol. 52, 1974, pp. 654+.

This article examines the reactions and defense of a federal agency of its decision not to comply with the provisions of NEPA due to the contention that its action does not fall within the confines of a "major federal action significantly affecting the quality of the human environment."

"Environmental Law: Statutory Construction—The California Environmental Quality Act, Requiring An Environmental Impact Report on Projects Having a Significant Effect on the Environment, Applies To Private Construction Projects Requiring a Government Permit As Well As To Public Projects," UNIVERSITY OF CINCINNATI LAW REVIEW, Vol. 43, 1973, pp. 563+.

The article makes three points with respect to the court's ruling in Friends of Mammoth v. Board of Supervisors Mono County. First, the court's interpretation of CEQA is a strained one; second, the problem raised by the case is not the type CEQA was intended to deal with; third, the extension of the CEQA to private projects leads to its application as a zoning variance, a use for which it specifically was not intended. The decision in this case which extends the impact statement filing requirements at the state level to private projects in an extremely important one.

"Environmental Law—Substantial Compliance with NEPA's 'Impact Statement' Requirement—A Look at Judicial Interpretation," OKLAHOMA LAW REVIEW, Vol. 26, 1973, pp. 281+.

This note considers some of the pitfalls of environmental impact statements filed under NEPA. It briefly covers the substantive content of an impact statement, full disclosure under NEPA, and the future of the 1970 act.

"Environmental Protection—NEPA—The Second Circuit Creates New Substantive and Procedural Guidelines To Aid Agencies in Making Threshold Determinations Of The Need For An Impact Statement—Hanly v. Kleindienst, 471 F. 2d 823 (2d Cir. 1972), " TEXAS LAW REVIEW, Vol. 51, May 1973, pp. 1016+.

This article discusses the evolution of the "thumbnail sketch" fulfilling the requirement that agencies must develop a reviewable environmental record in the course of making the threshold determination that a full impact statement is necessary. The "thumbnail sketch" may be required even though ultimately no full impact statement is required.

"The EPA's New Rules Hurt City Planners," BUSINESS WEEK, December 7, 1974, p. 112+.

This article discusses the widening impact that new Environmental Protection Agency's regulations will have on land use and development.

Flamm, Barry R. "A Philosophy of Environmental Impact Assessment: Toward Choice Among Alternatives," JOURNAL OF SOIL AND WATER CONSERVATION, September-October 1973.

This article discusses how environmental impact statement assessments have been affected and suggests strategies for improvement.

"Getting At The Issues," PROGRESSIVE ARCHITECTURE, June 1974, pp. 82.

This article discusses a number of state required EIR's (Environmental Impact Reports) and their deficiencies. It evaluates strategies for improvement including a recommendation by the Building Research

Advisory Board to develop standards for evaluating impacts.

Greis, David T., "The Environmental Impact Statement: A Small Step Instead of a Giant Leap," 1973, 39 pp. in THE URBAN LAWYER, Vol. 5, Number 2, Spring 1973, Section on Local Government Law, American Bar Association.

This article explores the legal history of the environmental impact statement and the circumstances under which one is required; the application of EIS to projects begun prior to the 1970 Act and the scope of review available in the courts once an EIS has been filed.

"Judicial Review of a NEPA Negative Statement," BOSTON UNIVERSITY LAW REVIEW, Vol. 53, 1973 pp. 879+.

This casenote discusses the efforts to clarify the standards applicable to a determination that a proposed action does not have a significant effect upon the quality of the human environment. In an effort to make judicial response more predictable, the Court of Appeals for the Second Circuit has attempted, in Hanly v. Kleindienst, to clarify standards for judicial review, this action is herein analyzed as a procedural guideline.

Kross, Burton C., "Preparation Of An Environmental Impact Statement," UNIVERSITY OF COLORADO LAW REVIEW, Vol. 44, August 1972, pp. 81+.

This article uses a specific example of a "major Federal action significantly affecting the environment" in order to demonstrate the process which goes into the preparation of an environmental impact statement. It concludes with an analysis of this process including a critical discussion of some of the problems which the author feels exist in the federal legislation.

Lukey, Joan A., "NEPA's Impact Statement In The Federal Courts: A Case Study of NRDC v. Morton," ENVIRONMENTAL AFFAIRS, Vol. 2, 1973, pp. 807+.

This article discusses first the legislative construction of NEPA and the initial restrictions on the scope of judicial review instituted by the Federal courts. The second section examines NRDC v. Morton and its relation to other NEPA cases. Lastly, it considers recommendations for providing an effective forum for full judicial review of substantive matters under NEPA.

Lynch, Robert M., "Complying With NEPA: The Tortuous Path To An Adequate Environmental Impact Statement," ARIZONA LAW REVIEW, Vol. 14, 1972, pp. 717+.

The purpose of this article is to analyze the process that accompanies compliance with the EIS reporting requirement of NEPA by examining the issues that federal administrators have encountered in their attempts to conform with the act's mandate. The focus is primarily upon principles developed in NEPA cases. Circumstances that cause NEPA to be applicable to a given project are reviewed, and procedural and substantive preparation of an impact statement investigated.

"The Nebraska Environmental Protection Act: Effects and Implications For the Nebraska Community," CREIGHTON LAW REVIEW, Vol. 7, 1974, pp. 283+.

This article sketches the Nebraska Environmental Act, as well as federal legislation with respect to clean air, water quality, solid waste, and pesticides. In each area of federal legislation the article examines the appropriate Nebraska legislation, rules and regulations, examining how they respond to federal law and how they complement and serve federal goals. It additionally examines future trends. The article is a fairly decent description of state adoption of EIS policies which parallel those of the federal government and how state laws are instituted to pursue these aims.

Pearlman, Jeffery A., "Happy Result in Ocean County," WALL STREET JOURNAL, Vol. 182, September 27, 1973, p. 1.

A brief examination of the problems and impediments to the construction of a $250 million sewage treatment system posed by the requirements of NEPA. It deals specifically with the procedural difficulties surrounding environmental impact statements. The power of EIS is emphasized here.

"The Preparation of Environmental Impact Statements by State Highway Commissions," IOWA LAW REVIEW, Vol. 58, 1973, pp. 1268+.

This comment examines the current procedures of the Federal Highway Administration (FHWA) which delegates the responsibility for preparing the environmental impact statement to the state highway commission in applications for federal aid for a road construction project. An impact statement prepared by the Iowa Highway Commission for a proposed freeway near Iowa City is utitilized to examine whether or not this agency's existing procedures comply with NEPA and its court interpretations.

Roberts, James A., "Just What Is An Environmental Impact Statement?" URBAN LAND INSTITUTE, February 1974.

The objective of this paper is to provide a preliminary "working" answer to the question of "what is an environmental impact statement?" It seeks to accomplish this by examining the following factors: the purpose of an EIS and its relation to the development process; the national, state and local legislation that have led to the present requirements for EIS; and a set of recommendations for EIS and its use by the development community.

Robinson, Ernest E., "EIS: Environmental Impact Statement or Extraordinarily Involved Semantics?" NEW JERSEY BUSINESS, Vol. 19, January 1973, pp. 32+.

A glimpse of the reaction of the business community to the requirements of EIS and NEPA is contained here. As might be expected, the article reviews the commitments of the business community to environmental protection yet is critical of those components of EIS that business leaders feel are counter-productive.

Seeley, James J., "The National Environmental Policy Act: A Guideline for Compliance," VANDERBILT LAW REVIEW, Vol. 26, 1973, pp. 299+.

This article extracts from CEQ Guidelines, judicial decisions and agency regulations—the relevant criteria utilized in resolving major issues affecting the application of NEPA. Its major thrusts are: whether a "major federal action" is present; whether this action will "significantly affect" the environment; which agency must file the impact statement; which parties must prepare the statement; when the statement must be filed; and what the statement must contain.

OTHER

Armstrong, John, "A Systems Approach to Environmental Impact," 1972, 11 pp. in ENVIRONMENTAL IMPACT ANALYSIS: PHILOSOPHY AND METHODS, Report No. Wis-56-72-111. Wisconsin University, 1972, 165 pp.

The article suggests the application of systems analysis to EIS processing. It discusses potentially improved movement through the legislative morass as a result of the application of a "Space Time Analysis System."

Best, Judith A., THE NATIONAL ENVIRONMENTAL POLICY ACT AS A FULL DISCLOSURE LAW, Cornell University, Ithaca, New York, Cornell Energy Project, December 1972, 24 pp.

Best, Judith A., NEPA IMPACT STATEMENTS: AGENCY EFFORTS TO ESCAPE THE BURDEN, Cornell University, Ithaca, New York, Cornell Energy Project, June, 1972, 18 pp.

Bruno, L.S., SHELTER INDUSTRY GUIDELINES, ENVIRONMENTAL IMPACT STATEMENTS, National Association of Homebuilders, 1973, 21 pp.

This paper views the lack of data on natural features and systems and the apparent non-responsiveness of the public sector in terms of providing this data as a major impediment to the reconciliation of development and conservation interests. It takes the position that, of necessity, the private sector must develop this information and presents guidelines to provide the building industry with information and methods relevant to environmental matters.

Cook, Robert S., "Communicating in Impact Analysis," 1972, 3 pp., in ENVIRONMENTAL IMPACT ANALYSIS: PHILOSOPHY AND METHODS, Report No. Wis-SG-72-111. Wisconsin University, 1972, 165 pp.

The article describes a particular project in terms of environmental impact. While it is off the mark in terms of housing, it does include a hefty section on the importance of correlation of input from diverse sources in the EIS decision-making process.

Denver Regional Council of Governments, GUIDE TO PREPARATION OF ENVIRONMENTAL IMPACT STATEMENTS, Denver, Colorado, May 1973, 27 pp.

The document is intended to assist in the preparation of EIS's which must be reviewed by COG's when there is a formal request for federal aid at county and local level.

Ditton, Robert B.; Goodale, Thomas L., ENVIRONMENTAL IMPACT ANALYSIS: PHILOSOPHY AND METHODS, Proceedings of the Conference on Environmental Impact Analysis, Green Bay, Wisconsin, January 4-5, 1972, 165 pp. Report No. Wis-56-72-111.

Problems associated with NEPA, 1969, its EIS requirements and its implementation are discussed by members of state and federal agencies and educators.

Environmental Science Associates, ENVIRONMENTAL IMPACT REPORTS, Burlingame, California, 18 pp.

This document discusses a private consultant's approach to preparation of environmental impact reports. Following a description of national and California legislation requiring impact statements, comments are provided on the structure the EIS document must take.

ENVIRONMENTAL STATEMENT BEACH EROSION CONTROL STUDY ON MANATEE COUNTY, FLORIDA, Office of the Chief of Engineers, Washington, D.C., 1972, 37 pp.

This document is an in-depth analysis conducted by the U.S. Army Corps of Engineers to determine steps to be taken to resolve the beach erosion problem. While not particularly relevant to housing, the inclusive EIS is a clear explication of all alternatives to the proposed action.

Galantowicz, Richard E., "Things You Never Wanted to Know About Zoning and Now Are Being Forced to Ask" in THE PROCESS OF ENVIRONMENTAL ASSESSMENT—OPTIONS AND LIMITS, North Jersey Conservation Foundation, September 1973, 13 pp.

This paper is the first in a series of five prepared as practical aids to local officials regarding the process of environmental assessment and the use of that information in the municipal planning process. Simple guidelines for local EIS are included in the appendix.

Galantowicz, Richard E., "Natural Resource Inventory for Municipal Fun and Profit" in THE PROCESS OF ENVIRONMENTAL ASSESSMENT—OPTIONS AND LIMITATIONS, North Jersey Conservation Foundation, November 1972, 13 pp.

This paper is the second in the series of five and is concerned with how to do a natural resource inventory as a prerequisite to EIS. It assists the user in gathering the available data and relating it to a particular municipality. The appendix provides a model for a local natural resource inventory.

Galantowicz, Richard E., "It All Begins With Sunlight and Green Plants" in THE PROCESS OF ENVIRONMENTAL ASSESSMENT—OPTIONS AND LIMITATIONS, North Jersey Conservation Foundation, March 1973, 26 pp. and appendix.

This is the third in the series of five. It attempts to place in perspective the environmental/economic conflict and lobbies for environmental considerations to transcend those of the market.

Galantowicz, Richard E., "A House Is More Than A Home" in THE PROCESS OF ENVIRONMENTAL ASSESSMENT—OPTIONS AND LIMITATIONS, North Jersey Conservation Foundation, June 1973, 24 pp.

This is the fourth in the series of five. It deals with the social or "people oriented" concerns that recur most often in discussions and controversies about planning, zoning and development, i.e. quality of life, population, density, and discrimination. The report stresses that the "people" factors should not be overlooked in the local planning and zoning process.

Galantowicz, Richard E., "Listen to the Land" in THE PROCESS OF ENVIRONMENTAL ASSESSMENT—OPTIONS AND LIMITATIONS, North

Jersey Conservation Foundation, October 1973, 58 pp.

This is the fifth in a series of five. This last paper examines methods of combining those factors which comprise the term "socioenvironomics" (people, natural resources and money) and taking them into account when designing municipal zoning and subdivision regulations. Part Two of this paper examines the potential of individuals, agencies and consultants, involved in attempting to integrate natural resource data into municipal land use planning.

Goodale, Thomas L., "NEPA: Buckle Down or Buckle Under," Wisconsin Univ., Green Bay, Wis., 1972, 3 pp. in ENVIRONMENTAL IMPACT ANALYSIS: PHILOSOPHY AND METHODS, 1972, 165 pp. Report No. WIS-SG-72-111.

Basically philosophical comments on environmental quality. Although technology now supplies the tools for data assemblage, the data and its analysis serve only as guides to human decision-making—a largely discretionary area at best.

Johnston, Per K., "Social Aspects of Environmental Impact," Wisconsin Univ., Green Bay, Wis., 1972, 4 pp. in ENVIRONMENTAL IMPACT ANALYSIS: PHILOSOPHY AND METHODS, 1972, 165 pp., Report No. WIS-SG-72-111.

The article discusses the expansion of environmental impact assessment to include concerns for the social ramifications of any project under consideration. The effect of the project on lifestyles, behavior patterns and social structure is covered.

Leopold, L.B.; Clarke, F.E.; Hanshaw, B.B.; and Balsley, J.R., A PROCEDURE FOR EVALUATING ENVIRONMENTAL IMPACT, Geological Survey Circular 645, U.S. Department of the Interior, Washington, D.C., 1971, 13 pp.

This circular has developed an informaton matrix system to assess environmental impact. The matrix is based upon the determination that an Environmental Impact Statement consists of four items: an analysis of need for the proposed action, a description of the environment involved, a discussion of the pertinent details of the proposed action, and an assessment of probable impacts and rationale supporting the selected plan of action. This circular and matrix are directed primarily at the fourth item; assessment of probable impact. Matrix included.

Little (Arthur D.), Inc., TRANSPORTATION AND ENVIRONMENT: SYNTHESIS FOR ACTION, U.S. Department of Transportation,

Washington, D.C., April 1971, 63 pp.

The objective of this study is to analyze the impact of NEPA 1969 on the Department of Transportation and to provide a set of alternative actions which the Department could utilize in complying with the act. The report includes policy alternatives available for consideration of environmental factors and documentation of how to measure and evaluate environmental impacts. Its importance for the EIS participant is its clear statement of alternatives to the proposed action.

Milane, M.P., ENVIRONMENTAL IMPACT STATEMENT, Datatronic Systems Corp., Computer Sciences and Environmental Technology Div., Panorama City, Calif., January 1973, 8 pp.

A general overview of what the environmental impact statement (EIS) is, its purpose, contents of the statement, actions for which impact statements must be prepared, when and how it is prepared, the role of the U.S. Environmental Protection Agency (EPA) in impact statements, a brief outline of what an EIS looks like, and an introduction to what agency procedures are required for state and local review.

Orloff, Neil, "Suggestions for Improvement of the Environmental Impact Statement Program," Environmental Protection Agency, Office of Federal Activities, Washington D.C., 1972, 13 pp. in ENVIRONMENTAL IMPACT ANALYSIS: PHILOSOPHY AND METHODS, 1972, 165 pp. Report No. WIS-SG-72-111.

The article discusses the problems of review of environmental impact statements. Such problems as whether or not to prepare an environmental impact statement, writing it, circulating it, and integrating it in the decision making process, are covered.

Rahenkamp, Sachs, and Wells, REVISED IMPACT ZONING ORDINANCE FOR DUXBURY, MASSACHUSETTS. Philadelphia, Pennsylvania, 1973.

Sabhlok, Andrew, SUGGESTED GUIDELINES FOR ENVIRONMENTAL IMPACT STATEMENTS, Associated Home Builders of the Greater East Bay Inc., Berkeley, California, 1972, 52 pp.

This document briefly summarizes the various laws pertaining to the environment at the time. Two examples of environmental impact statements prepared under its own guidelines are the document's enduring virtues.

Sager, Paul, "Conceptualizing Environmental Impact" Wisconsin Univ., Green Bay, Wis., 1972, 3 pp. in ENVIRONMENTAL IMPACT ANALYSIS: PHILOSOPHY AND METHODS, 1972, 165 pp. Report No. WIS-SG-72-111.

This article deals with the necessity to accept a philosophy of environmental values as a precursor to the formulation of guidelines for the curtailment of activity detrimental to the environment. For those of lofty rather than practical mind.

Shanfelt, D.Y.; Choate, D.A.; Yanada II, A.D., THE REFERRAL PROCESS: A DECISION MAKING SYSTEM FOR LAND USE MANAGEMENT, Environmental Control Division, Department of Community Development, City of Lakewood, Colorado, December 1973, 26 pp.

This pamphlet outlines the steps necessary for an effective and efficient environmental impact statement at the local level. The "Referral Process" has the capacity to respond to state and federal requirements while maintaining land use control at the local level. The pamphlet is an example of local response to the complexities of the multiple layers of government involved in EIS.

Sorenson, Jens C., "Some Procedures and Programs for Environmental Impact Assessment" Wisconsin Univ., Green Bay, Wis., 1972, 10 pp. in ENVIRONMENTAL IMPACT ANALYSIS: PHILOSOPHY AND METHODS, 1972, 165 pp. Report No. WIS-SG-72-111.

The report discusses the problems of relating the actions of a proposed project to possible changes of environmental conditions in light of the continued expansion of environmental considerations.

Sorenson, Jens C.; Pepper, James E., PROCEDURES FOR REGIONAL CLEARINGHOUSE REVIEW OF ENVIRONMENTAL IMPACT STATEMENTS, University of California, Los Angeles, October 1972, 124 pp.

The report presents a methodology for regional clearinghouse review of environmental impact statements as specified by the National Environmental Policy Act and/or the California Environmental Quality Act. Through network analysis the procedure systematically relates actions or activities of specified project-types to potential adverse environmental and socioeconomic impacts.

Sorensen, Jens C.; Moss, Mitchell L., PROCEDURES AND PROGRAMS TO ASSIST IN THE ENVIRONMENTAL IMPACT STATEMENT PROCESS, University of Southern California, Los Angeles, Sea Grant Program, April 1973, 45 pp.

The authors consider issues which arise in impact assessment processes and examine alternative methods for preparing and reviewing impact statements.

Stover, Lloyd V., ENVIRONMENTAL IMPACT ASSESSMENT: A

PROCEDURE, Technical Publications Section, Sanders and Thomas Inc., Pottstown, Pa., May 1972, 25 pp.

This pamphlet considers three questions basic to environmental impact assessment: what is the present state of the environment in a given area; what will be the effect of the new development, new product or new project on the existing environment? Considering pros and cons is the project worth doing. Again, this is an example of the private market approach to EIS.

Tryzna, Thaddeus C., ENVIRONMENTAL IMPACT REQUIREMENTS IN THE STATES, Office of Research and Development, U.S. Environmental Protection Agency, Washington, D.C., June 1973, 20 pp.

This study briefly reviews the requirements of environmental impact analysis for each of the various states. The study, one of the first done, summarizes what states have "little NEPA's" and whether or not private developments are included under EIS aegis.

Wacht, Samuel D., ENVIRONMENTAL IMPACT ASSESSMENT, A NEW APPROACH, from speech to National Association of Homebuilders, 1973, 9 pp.

The speech outlines the framework for guidelines which might be instituted to determine whether a project might have a significant effect on the environment. The guidelines have been promulgated by the California State Resources Agency.

Environmental Information Sources:
A Selected Bibliography

The source for information in this section is Carole Schildhauer, *Environmental Information Sources, Engineering and Industrial Applications: A Selected Bibliography*, New York, Special Libraries Association, 1972.

ABSTRACTS AND INDEXES

Abstracts on Health Effects of Environmental Pollutants
Philadelphia: Biosciences Information Service. Monthly. $95/year.

Acoustics Abstracts.
London: Multi-Science. Bi-monthly. $62/year.

Air Pollution Abstracts.
Research Triangle Park, N.C.: Air Pollution Technical Information

Center. Monthly. $21/year.

ASCA Topics.
Pittsburgh: Institute for Scientific Information. Weekly. $95/year.

Chemical Industry Notes (CIN).
Columbus, Ohio: Chemical Abstracts Service. Weekly. $300/year.

Environment Information Access.
New York: Environment Information Center. Bi-weekly. $150/year.

Environmental Periodicals.
Santa Barbara: Environmental Studies. 9 times a year. $55/year

Hydata.
Urbana: American Water Resources Association. Monthly. $55/year (library rate).

Institute of Paper Chemistry. Abstract Bulletin. Appleton, Wisconsin: I.P.C. Monthly. $30/vol.

Oceanic Instrumentation Reporter and Ocean Engineering.
La Jolla: Ocean Engineering Information Service. Monthly. $15/year.

Pollution Abstracts.
La Jolla: Pollution Abstracts. Bi-monthly. $70/year.

Selected Water Resources Abstracts.
Springfield, Va.: NTIS (for Water Resources Scientific Information Center). Semi-monthly. $22/year.

Transportation Noise Bulletin; Abstracts of Reports and Resumes of Research Projects Dealing with Transportation Noise.
Washington, D.C.: Transportation Noise Research Information Service. Semi-annual. $8/year.

Water Pollution Abstracts.
London: H.M.S.O. Monthly. $12/year.

Water Resources Abstracts.
Urbana: American Water Resources Association. Monthly. $120/year.

BIBLIOGRAPHIES AND CATALOGS

Anglemyer, Mary.
   The Human Environment. Washington, D.C.: Woodrow Wilson International Center for Scholars, 1972. 2 vol. $10.

Battelle Memorial Institute, Columbus, Ohio.
   Corrosion and Deposits From Combustion Gases: Abstracts and Index. New York: American Society of Mechanical Engineers, 1970. 300pp.

Bibliography of Doctoral Research in Ecology and the Environment.
   Ann Arbor: University Microfilms. Free.

Meshenberg, M.J.
   Environmental Planning: A Selected Annotated Bibliography. Chicago: American Society for Planning Officials, 1970. 79pp. $6.

Moulder, D.S. and A. Varley, comps.
   A Bibliography on Marine and Estuarine Oil Pollution. Plymouth, England: Marine Biological Association of the United Kingdom, 1971. 137pp. $7.50.

Ocean Affairs.
   Washington, D.C.: Woodrow Wilson International Center for Scholars, 1971. 201pp. $1.25.

Oil Pollution; An Index-Catalog to the Collection of the Oil Spill Information Center.
   Santa Barbara: University of California, Oil Spill Information Center, 1972. 4 vol. $275.

Sinha, Evelyn.
   Ocean Engineering Information Series. La Jolla: Ocean Engineering Information Service.

Transportation Masterfile 1921-1971.
   Washington, D.C.: U.S. Historical Documents Institute, 1972. $3,420.

Water Publications of State Agencies.
   Port Washington, N.Y.: Water Information Center, 1972. 350 pp. $39.50.

Werner, Jack and Lillian Roth.
   Air Pollution in the Pulp and Paper Industry. Appleton, Wisconsin: Institute of Paper Chemistry, 1969. 224 pp.

Winton, N.M.
   Man and the Environment. New York: Bowker, 1972. 326 pp. $12.50.

DIRECTORIES, YEARBOOKS, AND GUIDES

Air Pollution Control Association.
   APCA Directory and Resource Book. Pittsburgh: APCA.

American Water Works Association.
   AWWA Yearbook. New York: AWWA.

Clean Air Yearbook.
   London: National Society for Clean Air.

Directory of Environmental Educational Facilities.
   New York: National Audubon Society. Nature Center Planning
   Division, $2.

Directory of Governmental Air Pollution Agencies.
   Pittsburgh: Air Pollution Control Association, 1970. 63 pp. $2.50.

*A Directory of Information Resources in the United States: Physical
Sciences, Engineering.*
   Washington, D.C.: G.P.O., 1971. 803 pp. $6.50.

A Directory of Information Resources in the United States: Water.
   Washington, D.C.: G.P.O., 1966. 248pp. $1.50.

*Directory of National Organizations Concerned with Land Pollution Control,
1972.*
   New York: Freed, 1972. $8.

Ecology USA.
   New York: Special Reports, Inc., 1971. 624pp. $125.

Environmental Pollution; A Guide to Current Research.
   New York: CCM Information Corporation, 1971. 851pp. $25.

Industrial Water Engineering.
   Air/Water Engineering Buyers Guide and Directory. New York: Select
   Publications.

*Massachusetts Directory of Water Pollution Control Consulting Engineering
Firms.*

Amherst: University of Massachusetts, Technical Guidance Center for Industrial Environmental Control, 1970. 54pp.

Mordy, Wendell A. and Phyllis A. Sholtys, comps.
Directory of Organizations Concerned with Environmental Research. Fredonia, New York: Lake Erie Environmental Studies, State University College, 1970. 150pp. $2.

National and International Environmental Monitoring Activities—A Directory.
Washington, D.C.: Smithsonian Institution, 1970. 292pp. $10.

National Foundation for Environmental Control.
Directory of Environmental Information Sources. Boston: Cahners, 1972. 460pp. $25.

Pollution Analyzing and Monitoring Instruments—1972.
Park Ridge, N.J.: Noyes Data Corporation, 1972. 354pp. $36.

Pollution Control Directory.
Washington, D.C.: American Chemical Society.

U.S. Library of Congress. Congressional Research Service.
Environmental Science Centers at Institutions of Higher Learning. Washington, D.C.: U.S. Congress, House Committee on Science and Astronautics, Subcommittee on Science, Research and Development, 1969. Free.

University of California at Berkeley. Lawrence Berkeley Laboratory. Environment Instrumentation Group. *Instrumentation for Environmental Monitoring.* 4 vol. $7/each.

Water and Pollution Control Directory.
Don Mills, Ontario: Southam Business Publications.

Water Pollution Control Federation.
Directory. Washington, D.C.: WPCF.

Who's Who in Ecology.
New York: Special Reports, Inc.: Fall 1972. $50.

Encyclopedias, Dictionaries, Atlases

Firth, Frank E., editor.
Encyclopedia of Marine Resources. New York: Van Nostrand-Reinhold, 1969. 740pp. $25.

Fairbridge, Rhodes W., editor.
Encyclopedia of Atmospheric Sciences and Astrogeology. New York: Reinhold, 1968. 1200pp. $37.50.

Gilpin, Alan.
Dictionary of Fuel Technology. New York: Philosophical Library, 1969. 275pp. $20.

Glossary: Water and Wastewater Control Engineering.
New York: American Public Health Association, 1969. 387pp. $10.50.

Handbook of Effects Assessment: Vegetation Damage.
University Park, Pa.: Pennsylvania State University, Center for Air Environment Studies, 1969. $6.

McCrone, Walter, Ronald G. Draftz and John G. Delly.
The Particle Atlas: A Photomicrographic Reference for the Microscopical Identification of Particulate Substances. Ann Arbor: Ann Arbor Science, 1967. 406pp. $125.

Recognition of Air Pollution Injury to Vegetation: A Pictorial Atlas.
Pittsburgh: Air Pollution Control Association, 1970. 112pp. $15.

Serial Atlas of the Marine Environment, Folio 18: Wildlife Wetlands and Shellfish Areas of the Atlantic Coastal Zone.
Washington, D.C.: American Geographical Society, 1969. $12.

Veatch, J.O.
Water and Water Use Terminology. Kaukauna, Wis.: Thomas Printing Co., 1966. 375pp.

HANDBOOKS AND MANUALS

Air Pollution Engineering Manual.
Washington, D.C.: U.S. Department of HEW, 1967. 892pp.

Air Pollution Manual.
Detroit: American Industrial Hygiene Association, 1968. 2 vol.

American Water Works Association.
Water Quality and Treatment; A Handbook of Public Water Supplies, 3rd edition.

Ciaccio, Leonard, editor.
Water and Water Pollution Handbook. New York: Dekker, 1971/72. 4 vol. $110.

Eckenfelder, W. Wesley, editor
Manual of Treatment Processes. Stamford, Conn.: Environmental Science Services, 1970.

Hilado, Carlos J.
Handbook of Environmental Management. Wesport, Conn.: Technomic.

Lund, Herbert F.
Industrial Pollution Control Handbook. New York: McGraw-Hill, 1971. $29.50.

Ruch, Walter E.
Quantitative Analysis of Gaseous Pollutants. Ann Arbor: Ann Arbor Science, 1970. 241pp. $18.75.

Standard Methods for the Examination of Water and Wastewater.
13th edition. New York: American Public Health Association, 1971. 874pp. $22.50.

JOURNALS

AMBIO: A Journal of the Human Environment—Research and Management.
Oslo: Universitetsforlaget. Bi-monthly. $13/year.

Chemosphere.
New York: Pergamon. Bi-monthly. $35/year.

Critical Reviews in Environmental Control.
Cleveland: CRC Press. Quarterly. $56/Year.

Environmental Science and Technology.
Washington, D.C.: American Chemical Society. Monthly. $9/year.

The Science of the Total Environment: An International Journal for Scientific Research into the Environment and its Realtionship With Man.
New York: Elsevier. Bi-monthly. $27/year.

Water, Air and Soil Pollution; An International Journal of Environmental Pollution.
Dordrecht: D. Reidel. Quarterly. $43.95/year.

Air and Water News; Weekly Report on Environmental Pollution: the Law, the Markets, the Technology.
Detroit: Stanley H. Brams. Weekly. $145/year.

NEWSLETTERS

Air/Water Pollution Report.
  Silver Spring, Md.: Business Publishers, Inc. Weekly. $120/year.

Clean Air and Water News.
  Chicago: Commerce Clearing House. Weekly. $100/year.

Clean Water Report.
  Silver Spring, Md.: Business Publishers, Inc. Monthly. $24/year.

Coastal Zone Management.
  Washington, D.C.: Nautilus Press. Monthly. $90/year.

Ecologue.
  Boston: Associated Industries. Monthly. $7/year.

Environment Action Bulletin.
  Emmaus, Pa.: Rodale Press. Weekly. $10/year.

Environment Reporter.
  Washington, D.C.: Bureau of National Affairs. Weekly. $340/year.

Environmental Quality Report.
  Arlington, N.J.: Girard Associates. Semi-monthly. $50/year.

Environmental Technology and Economics.
  Stamford, Conn.: Environmental Science Services. Bi-weekly. $60/year.

Ground Water Newsletter.
  Port Washington, N.Y.: Water Information Center. Semi-monthly.
  $50/year.

Marine Information Transmitter.
  Cambridge: M.I.T. Sea Grant Project Office. Monthly. Free.

Marine Resources Digest/Marine Biology Digest.
  Arlington, N.J.: Girard Associates. Monthly. $30/year.

New England Marine Resources Information.
  Narragansett, R.I.: NEMRIP. Monthly. Free.

New England River Basins Commission Newsletter.
  Boston: NERBC. Monthly. Free.

Noise Control Report.

Silver Spring, Md.: Business Publications. Bi-weekly. $60/year.

Ocean Science News.
Washington, D.C.: Nautilus Press. Weekly. $165/year.

On Station.
Washington, D.C.: Nautilus Press. Weekly. Free.

Reuse/Recycle Newsletter.
Westport, Conn.: Technomic. Monthly. $25/year.

Sea Grant 70's.
College Station, Texas: Texas A and M University, Sea Grant Program Office. Monthly. Free.

Solid Waste Report.
Silver Spring, Md.: Business Publishers, Inc. Bi-weekly. $60/year.

Special Report Ecology.
New York: Special Reports, Inc. Weekly. $135/year.

World Ecology 2000-Ecosystems and Environmental Management.
Washington, D.C.: Nautilus Press. Bi-weekly. $125/year.

Symposia and Continuing Series

Advances in Ecological Research.
New York: Academic. vol. 1, 1962+.

Advances in Environmental Science and Technology.
New York: Wiley, vol. 1, 1969+.

Advances in Water Pollution Research.
New York: Pergamon. 1962+.

Air Pollution Control Association.
Proceedings Digest. Pittsburgh: APCA.

Institute of Environmental Sciences.
Proceedings of the Annual Meeting, Mt. Prospect, Ill. I.E.S., 1954+.

OTHER SOURCES

Air Sampling Instruments (for Evaluation of Atmospheric Contaminants), 3rd edition.
Cincinnati: American Conference of Governmental Industrial

Hygienists, 1969. 505pp.

Beranek, Leo.
Noise and Vibration Control, revised edition. New York: McGraw-Hill, 1971. 650pp.

Brahtz, J. F. Peel, editor.
Coastal Zone Management: Multiple Use with Conservation. New York: Wiley, 1972. 352pp. $19.95.

Cleaning Our Environment: The Chemical Basis for Action.
Washington, D.C.: American Chemical Society, 1969. 250pp. $2.75.

Degler, Stanley and Sandra C. Bloom.
Federal Pollution Control Programs: Water, Air and Solid Wastes. Washington, D.C.: BNA Books, 1971. 176pp. $4.

Dugan, Patrick R.
Biochemical Ecology of Water Pollution. New York: Plenum, 1972. 159pp. $14.50.

Franks, Felix, editor.
Water: A Comprehensive Treatise. New York: Plenum, June 1972+, 4 vol.

Important Chemical Reactions in Air Pollution Control.
New York: American Institute of Chemical Engineers, 1971. 92pp. $15.

James, George V.
Water Treatment; A Survey of Current Methods of Purifying Domestic Supplies and of Treating Industrial Effluents and Domestic Sewage, 4th edition. Cleveland: CRC Press, 1971. 320pp. $25.

Leithe, Wolfgang
The Analysis of Air Pollutants. Ann Arbor: Ann Arbor Science, 1970. 304pp. $18.75.

Matthews, William H., W. Kellogg and G. D. Robinson, editors.
Man's Impact on the Climate, Cambridge: MIT Press, 1971. 594pp. $17.50.

Murdoch, William W., editor.
Environment; Resources, Pollution and Society. Stamford, Conn.: Sinauer, 1971. 440pp. $5.95.

Pollution Control Review.
Park Ridge, New Jersey: Noyes Data Corporation, No. 1, 1970+.

Redmond, John C.
Clearing the Air; The Impact of the Clean Air Act on Technology. New York: IEEE, 1971. 158pp. $8.95.

Ross, Richard D., editor.
Industrial Waste Disposal. New York: Reinhold, 1968. 340pp. $16.

Society of Automotive Engineers.
Vehicle Emissions, Parts I, II, III. New York: Society of Automotive Engineers. 3 vol. $45.

Stern, Arthur C., editor.
Air Pollution, 2nd edition. New York: Academic, 1968. 3 vol. $95.

Strauss, Werner, editor.
Air Pollution Control, Parts 1 and 2. New York: Wiley, 1972.

Thomann, Robert V.
Systems Analysis and Water Quality Management, Stamford, Conn.: Environmental Science Services, 1970. $16.50.

Zajic, J.E.
Water Pollution: Disposal and Reuse. New York: Dekker, 1971. 2 vols. Vol. 1—$22.75; Vol. 2—$16.50.

PART II: PUBLIC AND PRIVATE ENVIRONMENTAL ORGANIZATIONS: A SELECTED LISTING

The source for information in this section is Carole Schildhauer, *Environmental Information Sources, Engineering and Industrial Applications: A Selected Annotated Bibliography,* New York, Special Libraries Association, 1972.

Public-Professional-Academic Information Sources

Air Pollution Control Association
4400 Fifth Avenue
Pittsburgh, Pennsylvania 15213
Telephone: (412) 621-1100

American Public Works Association
Institute of Solid Wastes
1313 East 60th Street
Chicago, Illinois 60637
Telephone: (312) 324-3400

American Society of Sanitary Engineering
228 Standard Building
Cleveland, Ohio 44113
Telephone: (216) 621-8520

American Water Works Association
2 Park Avenue
New York, New York 10016
Telephone: (212) 686-2040

Association of State and Interstate Water
    Pollution Control Administrators
P.O. Box 11143
Richmond, Virginia 23230
Telephone: (703) 770-2241

Committee for Environmental Information
438 North Skinker Boulevard
St. Louis, Missouri 63130
Telephone: (314) 863-6560

Connecticut University
Institute of Water Resources
Storrs, Connecticut 06268
Telephone: (203) 429-9321 ext. 474

Environmental Protection Agency
Project Documerica
Office of Public Affairs, EPA
Waterside Mall, Washington, D.C.
Attn: Gifford Hampshire

Florida University
Environmental Engineering Research Center
Gainesville, Florida 32601
Telephone: (904) 392-0834

Franklin Institute Research Laboratories
IDRES Information Center
(Institute for the Development of Riverine

and Estuarine Systems)
Benjamin Franklin Parkway at 20th Street
Philadelphia, Pennsylvania 19103
Telephone: (215) 448-1485

Maryland University
Water Resources Research Center
Shriver Laboratory
College Park, Maryland 20740
Telephone: (301) 454-3901

Midwest Research Institute
Environmental Pollution Center
425 Volker Boulevard
Kansas City, Missouri 64110
Telephone: (816) 561-0202

National Foundation for Environmental Control
151 Tremont Street
Boston, Mass. 02111
Telephone: (617) 426-0476

National Marine Water Quality Laboratory
Federal Water Quality Administration
U.S. Department of the Interior
Liberty Lane at Fairgrounds Road
P.O. Box 277
West Kingston, Rhode Island 02892
Telephone: (401) 789-9738

National Water Institute
744 Broad Street, Room 3405
Newark, New Jersey 07102
Telephone: (201) 623-1727

New England Interstate Water Pollution
    Control Commission
73 Tremont Street, Room 950
Boston, Mass. 02108
Telephone: (617) 742-0281

Pittsburgh University
Department of Civil Engineering
325 Engineering Hall
Pittsburgh, Pennsylvania 15213
Telephone: (412) 621-3500

EIS Substantive Areas and Information Sources

The County of Suffolk, New York, Council on Environmental Quality was the source for material in this section. Note that while state-county agencies are cited, appropriate local governmental bodies should be contacted as well.

1) *topography and land use*
   a)   land relief maps
> State-County Department of Planning; U.S. Geological Survey Maps (updated 7½ minute quads)
   b)   water bodies maps
> State-County Department of Planning; National Oceanic and Atmospheric Administration (formerly U.S. Coast & Geodetic Survey), U.S. Geological Survey
   quality
> State-County Department of Health (Division of Environmental Health Services), State-County Department of Environmental Control; U.S. Environmental Protection Agency (Water Quality Research), U.S. Geological Survey; Academic institution environmental research centers
   rates and currents
> State-County Department of Environmental Control; U.S. Environmental Protection Agency, U.S. Coast & Geodetic Survey, U.S. Corps of Engineers; Academic environmental research centers
   c)   watershed & drainage
> State-County Department of Environmental Control, Soil & Water Conservation Service, County Cooperative Extension; U.S. Geological Survey, U.S. Corps of Engineers, Academic environmental research centers
   groundwater
> State-County Department of Environmental Control, State-County Water Authority, State-County Department of Health; U.S. Geological Survey
   d)   physical setting
   types of land and land-use
> State-County Department of Planning, Soil and Water Conservation Service, State-County Department of Parks—Park Commission; National Park Service
   e)   existing roads
> State-County Department of Public Works, State-County Department of Planning; U.S. Geological Survey Topographic Maps (updated); State-County Department of Transportation; Hagstrom Atlas-County (if up to date)
   traffic information
> State-County Transportation Department, Department of

Traffic Safety
f)   climate
State-County Department of Environmental Control; U.S. Weather Bureau

2)   *present distribution of people (demography)*
State-County Department of Planning

3)   *biota (living organisms)*
a)   plant and animal communities
State-County Department of Environmental Conservation (Division of Fish & Game), (Director of Science Services); U.S. Fish & Wildlife Service; Academic environmental research centers, Museum of Natural History
b)   rare or endangered species and
species of commercial or recreational import
State-County Department of Parks, Recreation & Conservation; State-County Department of Environmental Conservation; U.S. Fish & Wildlife Service

4)   *minerals*
Soil & Water Conservation Service; U.S. Geological Survey, U.S. Corps of Engineers

5)   *soils*
State-County Department of Planning (soil maps)

6)   *pollution sources*
State-County Department of Health, State-County Department of Environmental Control; U.S. Environmental Protection Agency; U.S. Corps of Engineers
7)   *competing plans*
8)   *impact on man and nature*
a)   man
State-County Department of Planning, State-County Department of Environmental Control, Traffic Safety, State-County Department of Parks, Recreation & Conservation, Health; Cooperative Extension Service
b)   ecological systems
State-County Department of Environmental Protection-Conservation; U.S. Environmental Protection Agency, U.S. Fish & Wildlife Service; Academic environmental research centers
c)   historic settings and aesthetics
State-County Department of Planning, Department of Parks; Historic Landmarks Preservation

PART III: A GLOSSARY OF SELECTED ENVIRONMENTAL TERMS

The source for definitions is Office of Environmental Services, *Handbook for Environmental Commissioners*, Trenton, N.J., Department of Environmental Protection, January 1974.

ABATEMENT: The method of reducing the degree or intensity of pollution, also the use of such a method.

ABSORPTION: The penetration of a substance into or through another. For example, in air pollution control, absorption is the dissolving of a soluble gas, present in an emission, in a liquid which can be extracted.

ACCLIMATION: The physiological and behavioral adjustments of an organism to changes in its immediate environment.

ACTIVITATED SLUDGE PROCESS: The process of using biologically active sewage sludge to hasten breakdown of organic matter in raw sewage during secondary waste treatment.

ABSORPTION: The adhesion of a substance to the surface of a solid or liquid. Absorption is often used to extract pollutants by causing them to be attached to such absorbents as activated carbon or silica gel. Hydrophobic, or water-repulsing absorbents, are used to extract oil from waterways in oil spills.

AERATION: The process of being supplied or impregnated with air. Aeration is used in waste water treatment to foster biological and chemical purification.

AESTHETIC: That which people find beautiful or attractive. The quality of being aesthetic is not the opposite of the qualities of "practicality" or "reality," but rather another aspect or way of experiencing the same real world phenomena. Thus, blue skies, uncontaminated water, and uncluttered urban landscapes all have aesthetic impact, because they imply health, pleasure and security.

AIR CURTAIN: A method for mechanical containment of oil spills. Air is bubbled through a perforated pipe causing an upward water flow that retards the spreading of oil. Air curtains are also used as barriers to prevent fish from entering a polluted body of water.

AIR MASS: A widespread body of air with properties that were established while the air was situated over a particular region of the earth's surface and that undergoes specific modifications while in transit away from that region.

AIR POLLUTION: The presence of contaminants in the air in concentrations that prevent the normal dispersive ability of the air and that interfere directly or indirectly with man's health, safety or comfort or with the full use and enjoyment of his property.

AIR POLLUTION EPISODE: The occurrence of abnormally high concentrations of air pollutants usually due to low winds and temperature inversion and accompanied by an increase in illness and death.

AIR QUALITY CONTROL REGION: An area designated by the federal government where two or more communities—either in the same or different states—share a common air pollution problem.

AIR QUALITY STANDARDS: The prescribed level of pollutants in the outside air that cannot be exceeded legally during a specified time in a specified geographical area.

AIRSHED: The air overlying any arbitrary geographical region, frequently lumping together adjacent cities or areas which share intermixed air pollution problems.

ALGAL BLOOM: A proliferation of living algae on the surface of lakes, streams or ponds. Algal blooms are stimulated by phosphate enrichment.

AMBIENT AIR: Any unconfined portion of the atmosphere; the outside air.

ANTI-DEGRADATION CLAUSE: A provision in air quality and water quality laws that prohibits deterioration of air or water quality in areas where the pollution levels are presently below those allowed.

AQUIFER: An underground bed or stratum of earth, gravel or porous stone that contains water.

AQUATIC PLANTS: Plants that grow in water either floating on the surface, growing up from the bottom of the body of water or growing under the surface of the water.

AREA SOURCE: In air pollution, any small individual fuel combustion source, including any transportation sources. This is a general definition; area source is legally and precisely defined in federal regulations. See point source.

A-SCALE SOUND LEVEL: The measurement of sound approximating the auditory sensitivity of the human ear. The A-Scale sound level is used to measure the relative noisiness or annoyance of common sounds.

ASSIMILATION: Conversion or incorporation of absorbed nutrients into protoplasm. Also refers to the ability of a body of water to purify itself of organic pollution.

AUDIOMETER: An instrument for measuring hearing sensitivity.

BACKGROUND LEVEL: With respect to air pollution, amounts of pollutants present in the ambient air due to natural sources.

BACKGROUND RADIATION: Normal radiation present in the lower atmosphere from cosmic rays and from earth sources.

BAFFLE: Any deflector device used to change the direction of flow or the velocity of water, sewage or products of combustion such as fly ash or coarse particulate matter. Also used in deadening sound.

BAGHOUSE: An air pollution abatement device used to trap particulates by filtering gas streams through large fabric bags, usually made of glass fibers.

BALING: A means of reducing the volume of solid waste by compaction.

BALLISTIC SEPARATOR: A machine that separates inorganic from organic matter in a composting process.

BAND APPLICATION: With respect to pesticides, the application of the chemical over or next to each row of plants in a field.

BAR SCREEN: In waste water treatment, a screen that removes large floating and suspended solids.

BASAL APPLICATION: With respect to pesticides, the application of the pesticide formulation on stems or trunks of plants just above the soil line.

BENTHIC REGION: The bottom of a body of water. This region supports the benthos, a type of life that not only lives upon, but contributes to the character of the bottom.

BERYLLIUM: A metal that when airborne has adverse effects on human health; it has been declared a hazardous air pollutant. It is primarily discharged by operations such as machine shops, ceramic and propellant plants and foundries.

BIOASSAY: The employment of living organisms to determine the biological effect of some substance, factor or condition.

BIOCHEMICAL OXYGEN DEMAND (BOD): A measure of the amount of oxygen consumed in the biological processes that break down organic matter in water. Large amounts of organic waste use up large amounts of dissolved oxygen, thus the greater the degree of pollution, the greater the BOD.

BIODEGRADABLE: The process of decomposing quickly as a result of the action of microorganisms.

BIOLOGICAL CONTROL: A method of controlling pests by means of introduced or naturally occurring predatory organisms, sterilization or the use of inhibiting hormones, etc., rather than by mechanical or chemical means.

BIOMONITORING: The use of living organisms to test the suitability of effluent for discharge into receiving waters and to test the quality of such waters downstream from a discharge.

BIOSTABILIZER: A machine used to convert solid waste into compost by grinding and aeration.

BIOTA: All the species of plants and animals occurring within a certain area.

BOD: The amount of dissolved oxygen consumed in five days by biological processes breaking down organic matter in an effluent. See biochemical oxygen demand.

BOG: Wet, spongy land usually poorly drained, highly acid and rich in plant residue.

BOTANICAL PESTICIDE: A plant-produced chemical used to control pests; for example, nicotine, strychnine or pyrethrum.

BTU: "British thermal unit." The amount of heat required to raise the temperature of one pound of water one degree fahrenheit at its point of maximum density.

CARBON DIOXIDE (CO_2): A colorless, odorless, nonpoisonous gas that is a normal part of the ambient air. CO_2 is a product of fossil fuel combustion, and some researchers have theorized that excess CO_2 raises atmospheric temperatures.

CARBON MONOXIDE (CO): A colorless, odorless, highly toxic gas that is a normal byproduct of incomplete fossil fuel combustion. CO, one of the major air pollutants, can be harmful in small amounts if breathed over a certain period of time.

CARCINOGENIC: Cancer producing.

CATALYTIC CONVERTER: An air pollution abatement device that removes organic contaminants by oxidizing them into carbon dioxide and water through chemical reaction. Can be used to reduce nitrogen oxide emissions from motor vehicles.

CENTRIFUGAL COLLECTOR: Any of several mechanical systems using centrifugal force to remove aerosols from a gas stream.

CHANNELIZATION: The straightening and deepening of streams to permit water to move faster, to reduce flooding or to drain marshy acreage for farming. However, channelization reduces the organic waste assimilation capacity of the stream and may disturb fish breeding and destroy the stream's natural beauty, flood retention capability and ability to recharge aquifers.

CHEMICAL OXYGEN DEMAND (COD): A measure of the amount of oxygen required to oxidize organic and oxidizable inorganic compounds in water. The COD test, like the BOD test, is used to determine the degree of pollution in an effluent.

CHLORINATED HYDROCARBONS: A class of generally long-lasting, broad-spectrum insecticides of which the best known is DDT.

CHLORINATION: The application of chlorine to drinking water, sewage or industrial waste for disinfection or oxidation of undesirable compounds.

CLIMAX VEGETATION: The final, stable vegetation community in an ecosystem which will remain in an area if undisturbed.

COAGULATION: The clumping of particles in order to settle out inpurities; often induced by chemicals such as lime or alum.

COASTAL ZONE: Coastal waters and adjacent lands that exert a measurable influence on the uses of the sea and its ecology.

COD: See chemical oxygen demand.

COLIFORM INDEX: An index of the purity of water based on a count of its coliform bacteria.

COMBINED SEWERS: A sewerage system that carries both sanitary sewage and storm water runoff.

COMPOSTING: A controlled process of degrading organic matter by microorganisms.

DECIBEL: The unit of measurement of the intensity of sound.

DECOMPOSERS: Living plants and animals, chiefly fungi and bacteria, that live by extracting nutrients from the tissues of dead plants and animals. Vital to the life cycle.

DESICCANT: A chemical agent that may be used to remove moisture from plants or insects causing them to wither and die.

DEW POINT: The temperature at which a given percentage of moisture in the air condenses into droplets of water.

DIATOMACEOUS EARTH (DIATOMITE): A fine siliceous material resembling chalk used in waste water treatment plants to filter sewage effluent to remove solids.

DISSOLVED OXYGEN: Oxygen suspended in water in the form of microscopic bubbles.

DISSOLVED SOLIDS: The total amount of dissolved material, organic and inorganic, contained in water or wastes.

ECOLOGICAL IMPACT: The total of an environmental change, either natural or man-made, on the ecology of the area.

ECOLOGY: The interrelationships of living things to one another and to their environment or the study of such interrelationships.

ECOSYSTEM: An integrated unit or "system" in nature, sufficient unto itself with a balanced assortment of life forms, to be studied as a separate entity. Examples might be a rotting log in a forest, a pond, a coral atoll, a continent or the earth itself.

EFFLUENT: A discharge from an exit that is relatively self-contained such as an industrial smokestack, nuclear power plant, thermal plume or a sewage treatment plant. In common usage, referred to as a source of pollution, or as the pollution itself. Generally used in regard to discharges into waters.

EMISSION: See effluent. (Generally used in regard to discharges into air.)

EMISSION FACTOR: The average amount of a pollutant emitted from each type of polluting source in relation to a specific amount of material processed. For example, an emission factor for a blast furnace (used to make iron) would be a number of pounds of particulates per ton of raw materials.

EMISSION INVENTORY: A list of air pollutants emitted into a community's atmosphere, in amounts (usually tons) per day, by type of source. The emission inventory is basic to the establishment of emission standards.

EMISSION STANDARD: The maximum amount of a pollutant legally permitted to be discharged from a single source, either mobile or stationary.

ENVIRONMENT: The combination of all external influences and conditions affecting the life, development and ultimate survival of an organism, including man.

ENVIRONMENTAL QUALITY: Environmental quality refers to the properties and characteristics of the environment, either generalized or local, as they impinge on human beings and other organisms. Environmental quality is a general term which can refer to 1) varied characteristics such as air and water purity or pollution, noise, access to open space, and the visual effects of building and 2) the potential effects which such characteristics may have on physical and mental health.

ENVIRONMENTAL IMPACT ANALYSIS: The orderly and logical process by which the potential impact of a proposed development project on its immediate and more distant environments is analyzed. Types of analyses may range from impact on animal and plant life to impact on urban economy or health, depending on the nature and location of the development project.

ENVIRONMENTAL IMPACT STATEMENT: The actual presentation that results from an environmental impact analysis. It may be in the form of text, statistics, matrices, visual overlays, film, computer graphics and other graphic techniques, or a combination of any or all of these, depending on the client and the nature of the development project.

ERODIBILITY FACTOR: The "k" factor in the soil loss equations. The amount of soil which erodes from a standard experimental plot of bare soil under standard conditions of slope, rainfall, etc. It varies with the physical characteristics of the soil.

FECAL COLIFORM BACTERIA: A group of organisms common to the intestinal tracts of man and of mammals. The presence of fecal coliform bacteria in water is an indicator of pollution and of potentially dangerous bacterial contamination.

FILTRATION: In waste water treatment, the mechanical process that removes particulate matter by separating water from solid material usually by passing it through sand.

GREEN BELTS: Certain areas restricted from being used for buildings and houses; they often serve as separating buffers between pollution sources and concentrations of population.

GROUND COVER: Grasses or other plants grown to keep soil from being blown or washed away.

GROUNDWATER: The supply of fresh water under the earth's surface in an aquifer or soil that forms the natural reservoir for man's use.

GROUNDWATER RUNOFF: Groundwater that is discharged into a stream channel as spring or seepage water.

HABITAT: The sum total of environmental conditions of a specific place that is occupied by an organism, a population or a community.

HAZARDOUS AIR POLLUTANT: According to law, a pollutant to which no ambient air quality standard is applicable and that may cause or contribute to an increase in mortality or in serious illness. For example, asbestos, berylium and mercury have been declared hazardous air pollutants.

IMPLEMENTATION PLAN: A document of the steps to be taken to ensure attainment of environmental quality standards within a specified time period. Implementation plans are required by various laws.

INTERCEPTOR SEWERS: Sewers used to collect the flows from main and trunk sewers and carry them to a central point for treatment and discharge.

LEACHING: The process by which soluble materials in the soil, such as nutrients, pesticide chemicals or contaminants, are washed into a lower layer of soil or redissolved and carried away by water.

MASKING: Covering over of one sound or element by another. Quantitatively, masking is the amount the audibility threshold of one sound is raised by the presence of a second masking sound. Also used in regard to odors.

MGD: Millions of gallons per day. MGD is commonly used to express rate of flow.

MICROCLIMATE: Localized climatic conditions which are different from the regional climate.

MONITORING: Periodic or continuous determination of the amount of pollutants or radioactive contamination present in the environment.

NICHE: Both the physical place and the ecological role of an organism in a particular community.

pH: A measure of the acidity or alkalinity of a material, liquid or solid. pH is represented on a scale of 0 to 14 with 7 representing a neutral state, 0 representing the most acid and 14 the most alkaline.

PHYSIOGRAPHIC: The geographic and topographic characteristics of an area.

POINT SOURCE: In air pollution, a stationary source of a large individual emission, generally of an industrial nature.

POLLUTANT: Any introduced gas, liquid or solid that makes a resource unit for a specific purpose.

POLLUTION: The presence of matter or energy whose nature, location or quantity produces undesired environmental effects.

PPM: Parts per million.

PRIMARY TREATMENT: The first stage in waste water treatment in which substantially all floating or settleable solids are mechanically removed by screening and sedimentation.

PUMPING STATION: A station at which sewage is pumped to a higher level.

RECEIVING WATERS: Rivers, lakes, oceans or other bodies that receive treated or untreated waste waters.

RUNOFF: The portion of rainfall, melted snow or irrigation water that flows across ground surface and eventually is returned to streams. Runoff can pick up pollutants from the air or the land and carry them to the receiving waters.

SANITARY LANDFILLING: An engineered method of solid waste disposal on land in a manner that protects the environment; waste is spread in thin layers, compacted to the smallest practical volume and covered with soil at the end of each working day.

SANITARY SEWERS: Sewers that carry only domestic or commercial sewage. Storm water runoff is carried in a separate system. See sewer.

SECONDARY TREATMENT: Waste water treatment, beyond the primary stage, in which bacteria consume the organic parts of the wastes.

This biochemical action is accomplished by use of trickling filters or the activated sludge process.

SEDIMENTATION TANKS: In waste water treatment, tanks where the solids are allowed to settle or to float as scum. Scum is skimmed off; settled solids are pumped to incinerators, digesters, filters or other means of disposal.

SIGNIFICANT: In relation to environmental analysis, the term includes considerations of importance and magnitude, primarily the former.

SOIL LOSS EQUATION: Equation used to determine the amount of soil which will erode from a unit area over a year's time under varying conditions of rainfall, slope, etc.

SOLID WASTE MANAGEMENT: The purposeful, systematic control of the generation, storage, collection, transport, separation, processing, recycling, recovery and disposal of solid wastes.

STORM SEWER: A conduit that collects and transports rain and snow runoff back to the ground water. In a separate sewerage system, storm sewers are entirely separate from those carrying domestic and commercial waste water.

SUBJECTIVE: That which cannot be measured according to agreed upon standards or techniques. Whether or not such agreed upon standards or techniques exist is in no way related to the importance or significance of an environmental impact question.

SUBSTANTIAL: In relation to environmental analysis, the term "substantial" implies an impact which is sufficiently great to alter the basic nature or substance of an environmental system or element.

TERTIARY TREATMENT: Waste water treatment beyond the secondary, or biological stage that includes removal of nutrients such as phosphorus and nitrogen, and a high percentage of suspended solids. Tertiary treatment, also known as advanced waste treatment, produces a high quality effluent.

THERMAL POLLUTION: Degradation of water quality by the introduction of a heated effluent.

THRESHOLD DOSE: The minimum dose of a given substance necessary to produce a measurable physiological or psychological effect.

WATER POLLUTION: The addition of sewage, industrial wastes or other harmful or objectionable material to water in concentrations or in sufficient quantities to result in measurable degradation of water quality.

WATER QUALITY CRITERIA: The levels of pollutants that affect the suitability of water for a given use. Generally, water use classification includes: Public water supply; recreation; propagation of fish and other aquatic life; agricultural use; and industrial use.

WATER QUALITY STANDARD: A plan for water quality management containing four major elements: The use (recreation, drinking water, fish and wildlife propagation, industrial or agricultural) to be made of the water; criteria to protect those uses; implementation plans (for needed industrial-municipal waste treatment improvements) and enforcement plans; and an anti-degradation statement to protect existing high quality waters.

APPENDIX B:
EIS IN THE COURTS—PASSING THE
FEDERAL EXPERIENCE ON TO THE LOCAL LEVEL

INTRODUCTION

Since January 1, 1970, when the National Environmental Policy Act (NEPA)[1] went into effect, the law has generated enough litigation for the federal courts to hand down a NEPA decision on an average of once a week. Although only a few of these decisions have resulted in cancellations of a federal project on environmental grounds, the Council on Environmental Quality (CEQ) has reported that NEPA has had tremendous impact on agency decision-making "behind the scenes." The Corps of Engineers, for instance, claimed that 24 projects had been dropped, 44 temporarily or indefinitely delayed, and 197 significantly modified, as a result of the information obtained during the environmental impact statement preparation process.[2] Interceptor sewers in Rockland County, New York; oil and gas leases at Steamboat Lake, Colorado; and waste incinerators in Montgomery County, Maryland have all been cancelled because of NEPA—at least according to the CEQ.[3]

Yet the volume of suits alone, as well as the fact that most of the decisions have found the particular federal agency in violation of NEPA, would seem to suggest that for all the CEQ's self-congratulatory prose, the act is still less effective than its sponsors intended it to be. The purpose of this appendix is to explore the trends in litigation at the federal level as a prelude to what might be expected as judicial scrutiny by lower courts is extended to EIS filings. (There have been a number of important state supreme court decisions concerning filing under the "little NEPA's." See Jerome Rose, *New Directions in Planning Law: A Review of the 1972-1973*, 40 JOURNAL OF THE AMERICAN INSTITUTE OF PLANNERS 243, 248.)

APPLICATION

The section of a local ordinance that specifies the type of project for which an EIS must be prepared is probably the most important element. In most local ordinances which extend to private development, a threshold is established, such as the number of residential units or the square feet of nonresidential space, above which an applicant/developer is obligated to file.

For ordinances that extend the EIS filing requirement only to the public sector, the phrase "major action significantly affecting the quality of the human environment" is usually employed to determine applicability. This phrase minus the word "federal" comes directly from NEPA[4] and has had considerable litigation experience in federal agency EIS filings. The problem has been that neither the broad language of the statute, nor the CEQ guidelines,[5] really define the most important operative words: "major" and "significantly."

Once there is public involvement, an EIS will be required if the action is both "major" *and* one which "significantly affect(s) the quality of the human environment." In a widely-quoted passage, the Second Circuit noted:

Upon attempting . . . to interpret the amorphous term "significantly," . . . we are faced with the fact that almost every major federal action, no matter how limited in scope, has *some* adverse effect on the human environment. It is equally clear that an action which is environmentally important to one neighbor may be of no consequence to another. Congress could have decided that every major action must therefore be the subject of a detailed impact statement. . . . By adding the word "significantly," however, it demonstrated that before the agency in charge triggered that procedure, it should conclude that a *greater environmental impact would result than from "any major federal action."*[6] (emphasis added)

It is the clear trend in the decisions that "major" and "significant" are separate tests for the applicability of the EIS requirement, and that both qualities must be found.

In a few cases the courts have agreed with the federal agency's determination that although there was federal involvement in a project, it was not a "major" action: Operation Snowy Beach, a mock winter amphibious exercise in Maine's coastal Reid State Park;[7] the widening of a fourteen-block portion of Mt. Vernon Road in Cedar Rapids, Iowa;[8] the introduction of "stretch" jets into the National Airport in Washington, D.C.;[9] and the construction of a 4.3-mile, one-lane gravel road through a portion of Monongahela National Forest in West Virginia.[10]

The bulk of the cases, however, have concerned projects so huge that their being "a major action" (as well as "significantly affecting the quality of the human environment") was unquestioned: a 75-mile stretch of I-66 through Arlington County, Virginia;[11] the Gillham Dam project on Arkansas'

Cossatot River;[12] and a continuous barge waterway from the upper
Mississippi and Ohio river valleys to Mobile, Alabama, on the Gulf of
Mexico.[13] The range of "major actions" also includes: the approval of the
lease of Pueblo land in New Mexico;[14] a waterfront rehabilitation project in
Boston;[15] permission from the Interstate Commerce Commission to
abandon rail service in Brooklyn;[16] controlling fire ants in the Southwestern
United States;[17] and a high-rise apartment building for students in the
Goose Hollow area of Portland, Oregon.[18]

The question of whether a major project has a significant effect on the
human environment is at times simple to answer, as in the cases above, but
only because the answer is so very obvious. It is when the project is not as
enormous as a dam or a reservoir or highway that the decision becomes more
difficult. The Second Circuit has adopted the following:

> In the absence of any Congressional or administrative interpretation of
> the term, we are persuaded that in deciding whether a major federal
> action will "significantly" affect the quality of the human environment
> the agency in charge . . . should normally be required to review the
> proposed action in the light of at least two relevant factors: (1) the
> extent to which the action will cause adverse environmental effects in
> excess of those created by existing uses in the area affected by it, and
> (2) the absolute quantitative adverse environmental effects of the
> action itself, including the cumulative harm that results from its
> contribution to existing adverse conditions or uses in the affected area.
> Where a conduct conforms to existing uses, its adverse consequences
> will usually be less significant than when it represents a radical change.
> Absent some showing that an entire neighborhood is in the process of
> redevelopment, its existing environment, though frequently below an
> ideal standard, represents a norm that cannot be ignored. For instance,
> one more highway in an area honeycombed with roads usually has less
> of an adverse impact than if it were constructed through a roadless
> public park.[19]

This decision, as well as the preceding *Hanly I*,[20] and the later *Hanly III*[21]
should be read closely.

The analysis of whether a proposed project is major and has a significant
effect on the quality of the human environment is thus a preliminary or
"threshold" decision which the public agency must make, since if any one of
the elements is missing, no EIS will be required.

A public agency's decision that a particular project does not require an
EIS, because it is not a major action, or has no significant effect, or both, is
fortunately not a decision which the agency may make with unfettered
discretion. If it were, given the time, energy, and money which must be spent
on preparing an EIS, it seems likely that no EIS would ever be prepared. Yet
because there are activities of the government which do not meet the
standards laid down by NEPA or its progeny, agencies must have some

discretion over whether or not to prepare an EIS. A decision not to prepare an EIS at the federal level has usually been accompanied by a brief written "declaration of negative impact" or a "negative impact statement." Since this statement is essentially based on an analysis of whether the project is "major" and "significant," the "threshold" cases tend to revolve around the adequacy of the record prepared by the agency to justify its decision, and around the scope of judicial review of that decision.

It is only logical that there must be *some* record for a court to examine if an agency's determination not to prepare an EIS is to be successfully challenged, and it is equally logical that merely conclusory language is insufficient justification for such a determination. The outer limits of the extent of the required record have been completely clarified by the courts. In one instance, the Corps of Engineers, as construction agency for the U.S. Postal Service, determined that a new post office in Prince George's County, Maryland, would have no significant effect on the human environment.[22] From the description given in the case, the Corps' detailed environmental assessment sounds like the "mini-impact statement" described in Chief Judge Friendly's dissent in *Hanly II*, in which he argued that the Second Circuit's decision required too much of public agencies:

> ... the agency must go through procedures which I think are needed only when an impact statement must be made. The upshot is that a threshold determination that a proposal does not constitute a major Federal action ... becomes a kind of mini-impact statement.

> The preparation of such a statement under the conditions laid down by the majority is unduly burdensome when the action is truly minor or insignificant. On the other hand, there is a danger that if the threshold determination is this elaborate, it may come to replace the impact statement in the grey area between actions which, though "major" in a monetary sense, are obviously insignificant ... and actions that are obviously significant (such as the construction of an atomic power plant).[23]

The "mini-impact statement," or thumbnail sketch, would appear to be the maximum record the courts have required to serve as a basis for reviewing a threshold decision by a federal agency, while the minimum level has not yet been identified.

Once there is a reviewable record, the courts are also divided on the standard of review to be applied to a challenged threshold determination that an EIS is not necessary. Of the courts which have explicitly discussed the question, the Second and Fifth Circuits are examples of the two prevailing viewpoints. The Second Circuit applies the "arbitrary, capricious, abuse of discretion" standard,[24] while the Fifth Circuit says:

To best effectuate the Act (the agency's) decision should have been court-measured under a more relaxed rule of reasonableness, rather than by the narrower standard of arbitrariness or capriciousness.[25]

Assuming, then, that a public agency has either decided that an EIS is necessary, on its own, or else has been ordered to prepare one by a court that has rejected the agency's "declaration of negative impact," the next major question is who prepares the EIS.

WHO PREPARES THE EIS?

The responsibility for preparing an EIS has been discussed from a conceptual point of view in an earlier section of this handbook. Obviously there are legal issues involved here as well. Again the experience of federal agencies in filing impact statements provides some insight as to whom the courts have designated as responsible in the public sector. At the local level, however, where EIS is required of *private* projects the applicant/developer is almost uniformly tendered this responsibility. This in and of itself is an interesting transfer of responsibility, as the ensuing discussion will point up. Where local EIS's are required of primarily public or publicly funded projects, the agency initiating such a project or providing the funding is given the EIS filing responsibility. Local public sector filing procedure has perhaps the most to gain from the federal experience.

A public agency's consideration of environmental factors must obviously be done *before* the final decision is made on whether to proceed with a given project. It is equally obvious that, if the goals of NEPA and its progeny are to be attained, this consideration must be an objective one: the ultimate decision-maker must have all the relevant facts before him, presented with as little bias as is humanly possible.

Objective appraisal of environmental costs and benefits, as well as other technological, economic, physical, psychological, or social benefits, is the only logical "condition precedent" to an agency decision. It is unfortunate, therefore, that so many agencies make a practice of delegating responsibility for preparing an EIS to the state agency and/or private party who has initiated or wishes to initiate the project. Because of the ease with which an applicant who has virtually complete control over EIS preparation might slant information to minimize environmental costs and thus favor the project, the delegation question raises two issues: whether NEPA permits *any* delegation, and if so, what degree of federal agency participation in the process is necessary to insure compliance with the goals of NEPA.

The only circuit court of appeals to flatly prohibit any delegation, so far, is the Second Circuit, in *Greene County Planning Board v. Federal Power Commission*.[26] Citing the District of Columbia Circuit's landmark decision in *Calvert Cliff's Coordinating Committee v. AEC*,[27] the second Circuit approached the delegation question from a function-oriented analysis of NEPA. The court argued that while delegation may not interfere with the procedural aspects of EIS preparation (the mere *acts* of preparation, circulation, and consideration in the agency review process), delegation created a high potential for *substantive* failures in the content and quality of the EIS—a clear interference with the EIS function of providing objective evaluation of environmental aspects of a project. This risk is explained by the Second Circuit in terms of a lack of significant participation by a federal agency in the EIS process:

> The Federal Power Commission has abdicated a significant part of its responsibility by substituting the statement of PASNY (Power Authority of the State of New York) for its own. The Commission appears to be content to collect the comments of other federal agencies, its own staff and the intervenors and . . . act as an umpire. The danger of this procedure, and one obvious shortcoming, is the potential, if not the likelihood, that the applicant's statement will be based on self-serving assumptions.[28]

Three other circuits, however, while superficially recognizing the potential hazards of delegation, have still permitted it: the Eighth Circuit in *Iowa Citizens for Environmental Quality v. Volpe,*[29] the Ninth Circuit in *Life of the Land v. Brinegar,*[30] and the Tenth Circuit in *Citizens Environmental Council v. Volpe.*[31] The Supreme Court of the United States denied certiorari in both the latter decisions. Although there are other grounds for permitting delegation, most of the courts, at both the appellate and district levels, have relied on distinguishing the case at hand from *Greene County* by finding "significant agency participation" in the EIS process. The following excerpt from *Iowa Citizens* is a sample of the conclusions reached:

> The district court, upon the basis of substantial evidence, specifically found that the FHWA recommended changes in the initial statement and provided additional information to be added to the final statement. Review, modification and adoption by the FHWA of the statements as its own occurred in this case. Such extensive participation by the responsible agency would clearly distinguish this case from *Greene County*. In our present case, the federal agency did not "abdicate a significant part of its responsibility" to the State Highway Commission by "rubber stamping" or adopting an unaltered or incompletely reviewed environmental impact statement.[32]

Once the EIS has been prepared and distributed, it is next subject to attack in the courts on the question of its adequacy.

THE ADEQUACY OF AN EIS

There are four main areas which have been used by the courts as a basis for finding a particular EIS inadequate: lack of detail, failure to discuss alternatives, failure to consider opposing views, and obscuring the environmental effects of the proposed project.

Detail

> ... the EIS must be "marked by abundant detail or thoroughness in treating small items or parts"; ... Thus, [an EIS] must thoroughly discuss the *significant* aspects of the *probable* environmental impact of the proposed agency action. By definition, this excluded the necessity for discussing either insignificant matters, such as those without import, or remote effects, such as mere possibilities unlikely to occur as a result of the proposed activity. This criterion ... comports with a rule of reason; it does not, however, encompass the necessity of disclosing "all known possible environmental consequences". ... The EIS must be written in language that is understandable to non-technical minds and yet contain enough scientific reasoning to alert specialists to particular problems within the field of their expertise.[33]

The phrase "all known possible environmental consequences" used by Judge Keady refers to a broader test for the adequacy of detail, applied in *Environmental Defense Fund, Inc. v. Corps of Engineers*:

> At the very least, NEPA is an environmental full disclosure law. ... The "detailed statement" required by Sec. 102(2)(C) should, at a minimum, contain such information as will alert the President, the Council on Environmental Quality, the public, and, indeed, the Congress, to all known *possible* environmental consequences of the proposed agency action. ... The record should be complete. Then, if the decision-makers choose to ignore such factors, they will be doing so with their eyes wide open.[34]

It is implicit in both decisions, however, that the amount of detail necessary for a particular EIS must in reality be based on the complexity of the proposed project; as in the case of threshold decisions, merely conclusory language will not suffice. Two points key directly to local filings: (1) they must be complete statements, not merely brushing aside a substantive area of concern *with* an unsupported statement of "no impact," yet they need not be excessive, emphasizing every minute detail; and (2) they must be sufficiently general to be understood by a range of actors yet sufficiently detailed to adequately cover an area wherein an expert of specific competence may be called to attest to the statement's adequacy. Quite a charge for a local EIS!

Alternatives

With regard to the obligation to discuss alternatives to the project, again the federal filing experience may serve as a guide for local filings. One commentator has said that Sec. 102(2) (D) of NEPA:

... suggests that the consideration of alternatives must be as thorough as the consideration of environmental impact. If an environmentally harmless alternative exists, it must be adopted instead of the original proposal. Where the proposal has no alternative compatible with the national environmental policy, the legislative history suggests that federal officials and agencies have the responsibility to reassess the justification for the proposed action.[35]

A more moderate approach was taken by the District of Columbia Circuit in a suit to stop the lease-sale of submerged land off the Louisiana coast, for oil-drilling:

A sound construction of NEPA ... requires a presentation of the environmental risks incident to reasonable alternative courses of action. The agency may limit its discussion of environmental impact to a brief statement, when that is the case, that the alternative course involves no effect on the environment, or that the effect, briefly described, is simply not significant. A rule of reason is implicit in the requirement that the agency provide a statement concerning this aspect of the law as a statement concerning those opposing views that are responsible.[36]

The danger, of course, in requiring too detailed a discussion of alternatives is that the entire decision-making process would grind to a halt through the sheer weight of the data required for the EIS. It is also worth noting that a few cases suggest that the agency must consider alternatives to the project outside the scope of their authority. One author has suggested considering alternatives early in the EIS process and then preparing an EIS on the best several alternatives. Obviously, this is an awesome task, and at the local level where the EIS responsibility has been placed at the feet of the applicant/developer, an unreasonably expensive one.

Opposing Views

Since the function of the EIS is to alert agency decision-makers to the environmental consequences of a proposed project, the final EIS has to include responsible opposing views, and must in turn answer those comments. This is much more a public rather than private responsibility regardless of who initiates the EIS. Once the necessity for such information has been made clear to the agencies (by the courts), the agencies have generally responded with alacrity. In a suit to stop the New Hope Lake dam project in North Carolina, the court commented:

The primary reason that the impact statement meets the requirement of full disclosure is because the defendants included in the statement the depositions of plaintiffs' expert witnesses.[37]

Clarity of Environmental Effects

Because the size of the usual EIS is enormous, at a minimum a thick single volume, it would be relatively easy to hide the environmental effects of a project in a mass of verbiage, to bury the impacts in a welter of detail. One court even had to go so far as to establish guidelines for the preparation of the EIS for the 363-mile Trinity River Basin project, so that the court, when reviewing the EIS could clearly understand the impact of each segment of the decades-long project, and its relation to the whole, as well as the eventual total impact.[38] In fact, brutal frankness about the environmental effects may at times be an asset, as in the River Rouge Flood Control Project in Michigan. The Corps of Engineers bluntly and candidly summarized the effect of the project on one of the few remaining areas of wild greenery in Detroit:

> Practically no natural, productive wildlife habitat will survive if the project is implemented, and there will be a permanent loss to present recreational uses, and aesthetic qualities afforded by the open natural area.[39]

The EIS was found to be adequate.

SUBSTANTIVE REVIEW OF THE AGENCY DECISION

Once the EIS has been found to be adequate, those opposing the project have only one recourse left: to seek review of the agency decision on substantive, rather than procedural, grounds. Until November 1972, every decision construing NEPA had concluded that it was a procedural law only, and that once an agency had complied with the procedural requirements, the courts' function was at an end. The Eighth Circuit, however, in a continuation of the Gillham Dam controversy, said:

> ... The language of NEPA, as well as its legislative history, make it clear ... NEPA was intended to effect substantive changes in decisionmaking. ...

> The unequivocal intent of NEPA is to require agencies to consider and give effect to environmental goals set forth in the Act, not just to file detailed impact studies which will fill governmental archives. ...

> Given an agency obligation to carry out the substantive requirements of the Act, we believe that courts have an obligation to review substantive agency decisions on the merits. ...

> .. The reviewing court must first determine whether the agency acted within the scope of its authority, and next whether the decision

reached was arbitrary, capricious, an abuse of discretion, or otherwise not in accordance with law. In making the latter determination, the court must decide if the agency failed to consider all relevant factors in reaching its decision, or if the decision itself represented a clear error in judgment.[40]

Although this language would seem to hold promise for stopping projects in which, at least arguably, the cost-benefit ratio was weighted on the "cost" side environmentally, no case has been discovered in which a court overturned an agency's final decision to proceed with a given project. With the present concern over the state of our environment, however, *Gillham III* represents strong, if little-used, authority for substantive review of an agency's projects.

ONGOING PROJECTS

When NEPA first went into effect it created a great deal of confusion among the agencies about the "retroactivity" of its provisions, with reference to agency projects which had been started prior to January 1, 1970, but were not yet complete. This is particularly important in terms of the ability to require an EIS filing for major projects. Although a few of the early decisions flatly refused to apply the requirements of the act to a project begun before its effective date,[41] within two years most courts were applying a "balancing test" to determine whether the federal law should apply to a given project.

NEPA mandates a case-by-case balancing judgment on the part of federal agencies. In each individual case, the particular economic and technical benefits of planned action must be assessed and then weighed against the environmental costs. . . . (T)he magnitude of possible benefits and possible costs may lie anywhere on a broad spectrum. Much will depend on the particular magnitudes involved in particular cases. . . . The point of the individualized balancing analysis is to ensure that, with possible alterations, the optimally beneficial action is finally taken.[42]

This principle is supplemented by the Fourth Circuit's decision in the battle over Interstate 66 in Arlington, Virginia:

Doubtless Congress did not intend that all projects ongoing at the effective date of the Act should be subject to the requirements of Section 102. At some stage of progress, the cost of altering or abandoning the project could so definitely outweigh whatever benefits might accrue therefrom that it might no longer be "possible" to change the project in accordance with Section 102.[43]

It will usually be decided that the law *is* applicable to an ongoing project if there is still a substantial amount of work to be done, and if, realistically, there is an opportunity to reconsider (if necessary) aspects of that remaining work. Thus, where the benefits are not outweighed by the environmental costs, and the initiator will not suffer irreparable harm while an EIS is prepared for the ongoing project, or remaining segments of it, courts have usually issued injunctions halting all work until the EIS is prepared. Naturally, as the years pass, this will tend to become a dead issue for federal agency filings, but increasingly important for local filings under a variety of ordinance formats.

CURRENT TRENDS IN EIS LITIGATION

For all practical purposes, the outer parameters of NEPA have been defined by the early cases, which is why the preceding elements of this section have relied so much on those early decisions. The general principles are settled, and although the volume of NEPA litigation does not seem to have abated, most of the cases in 1973 and 1974 have dealt with the application of those principles to varying situations. It has become an almost mechanical process for courts to evaluate the adequacy of an EIS.

Yet there is a perceptible trend toward litigation involving the subtleties and nuances of NEPA. For instance, take the key NEPA phrase: "a major federal action significantly affecting the quality of the human environment." As indicated above, there has been a tremendous amount of litigation directly or indirectly involving the words "major" and "significant." Only now, a few cases are beginning to appear which take a closer look at the phrase, "human environment." As an estimate, between 96 and 98 percent of the NEPA cases concern man's physical environment: losses (or alleged losses) to birds and bees, to flowers and trees, to wildlife and open spaces; there is almost an aura of warfare between endangered living things, whether sentient or not, and brutal, steamroller technology in the name of "progress."

The remaining, very few, cases, beginning with *Hanly I and II* are evidencing a concern for man's social and psychological environment. *Hanly*, for example, considers the effect of a jail across the street from an apartment area upon the "human environment" of the neighborhood. *Nucleus of Chicago Homeowners Association v. Lynn*[44] considers the alleged negative sociological and psychological impact of tenants of public housing on a (presumably white) middle-class neighborhood. *Tierrasanta Community Council v. Richardson*[45] considers the impact of a 206-acre youth correctional facility within 500 feet of a proposed elementary school and essentially adjoining, or partially surrounded by, a low-density single-family residential neighborhood.

Another facet beginning to surface is concern for cumulative environmental impacts. *Sierra Club v. Froehlke*[46] concerns the Trinity River Basin project in southern Texas, a comprehensive development program which includes provisions for navigation, flood control, water conservation, and recreation. The project itself will consist of a 363-mile, 12 by 200 foot channel from Galveston Bay to Fort Worth, with sixteen navigation dams and twenty navigation locks. The district court has in essence ordered the Corps of Engineers and the other responsible agencies to prepare not only an EIS for each identifiable segment of the project, but for the project as a whole, showing how each segment relates to the totality, and how the environmental impact of each segment relates to the total impact when the project is completed. The channel will take many years to build, and it is entirely possible that an environmental analysis of each identifiable segment as it was constructed might show a balance of environmental benefits over costs, but unless the entire project is evaluated at the start, the cumulative negative impacts (if any) may build up so that, without such early evaluation, by the time the project is completed and the negative impacts are perceived nothing could be done to rectify them.

Another new area to which the EIS requirement is being applied is the research program. *Scientists' Institute for Public Information v. Atomic Energy Commission*[47] required an EIS for the AEC's research program into the feasibility of Liquid Metal Fast Breeder Reactors (LMFBR's) as an alternative source of energy:

> Taking into account the magnitude of the ongoing federal investment in this LMFBR program, the controversial environmental effects attendant upon future widespread deployment of breeder reactors should the program fulfill present expectations, the accelerated pace under which this program has moved beyond pure scientific research toward creation of a viable, competitive breeder reactor electrical energy industry, and the manner in which investment in this new technology is likely to restrict future alternatives, we hold that the Commission's program comes within both the letter and the spirit of Section 102(2)(C) and that a detailed statement about the program, its environmental impact and alternatives thereto is presently required.[48]

Implicitly, there are two areas which must be covered in this EIS: the environmental impact of the research program itself, and the environmental impact of the reactors, if built. This does not, of course, mean that no EIS would be necessary for each individual reactor as it was constructed.

CONCLUSION

The experience of federal agency EIS filings has significant bearing on what the future will hold for local equivalents.

This foregoing section has dealt with the issues of applicability, responsibility, retroactivity, and adequacy relating to federal agency EIS filings. Other legal texts have dealt with the issues of substantive rights, standing, definitional vagaries, and scope of review. Unfortunately, however, the subtleties being considered are essentially more of procedure than substance, and it is our opinion that until one court follows the lead given by the Eighth Circuit in *Gillham III* and actually invalidates a decision to proceed with a development despite environmental costs shown in the EIS, we have nothing more here than a *paper* tiger—and never has the term "paper" been used so literally.

NOTES

1. 42 U.S.C. 4321 et seq. (1970).

2. Council on Environmental Quality, *Fourth Annual Report* 237 (1973).

3. *Id*. at 247.

4. 42 U.S.C. 4332(2)(C).

5. 40 C.F.R. 1500 et seq. (1973).

6. Hanly v. Kleindienst, 471 F.2d 823, 830 (2d Cir. 1972) (Hanly II).

7. Citizens for Reid State Park v. Laird, 336 F. Supp. 783 (D. Me. 1972).

8. Julis v. City of Cedar Rapids, 349 F. Supp. 88 (N.D. Iowa 1972).

9. Virginians for Dulles v. Volpe, 344 F. Supp. 573 (E.D. Va. 1972).

10. Kisner v. Butz, 350 F. Supp. 310 (N.D.W. Va. 1972).

11. Arlington Coalition on Transportation v. Volpe, 458 F.2d 1323 (4th Cir. 1972).

12. Environmental Defense Fund, Inc. v. Corps of Engineers, 325 F. Supp. 749 (E.D. Ark. 1971) (Gillham I).

13. Environmental Defense Fund, Inc. v. Corps of Engineers, 331 F. Supp. 925 (D.D.C. 1971).

14. Davis v. Morton, 469 F.2d 593 (10th Cir. 1972).

15. Boston Waterfront Residents Ass'n., Inc. v. Romney, 343 F. Supp. 89 (D. Mass. 1972).

16. City of New York v. United States, 337 F. Supp. 150 (E.D. N.Y. 1972).

17. Environmental Defense Fund, Inc. v. Hardin, 325 F. Supp. 1401 (D.D.C. 1971).

18. Goose Hollow Foothills League v. Romney, 334 F. Supp. 877 (D. Ore. 1971).

19. Hanly II, *supra* note 6, at 830.

20. Hanly v. Mitchell, 460 F.2d 640 (2d Cir. 1972) (Hanly I).

21. Hanly v. Kleindienst, 484 F.2d 448 (2d Cir. 1973) (Hanly III).

22. Maryland-National Capital Park and Planning Comm'n. v. U.S. Postal Service, 349 F. Supp. 1212 (D.D.C. 1972).

23. Hanly II, *supra* note 6, at 837.

24. *Id*. at 830.

25. Save Our Ten Acres v. Kreger, 472 F.2d 463 (5th Cir. 1973).

26. 455 F.2d 412 (2d Cir.), *cert. denied*, 409 U.S. 849 (1972).

27. 449 F.2d 1109 (D.C. Cir. 1971).

28. Greene County, *supra* note 26, at 420.

29. 487 F.2d 849 (8th Cir. 1973).

30. 485 F.2d 460 (9th Cir. 1973).

31. 484 F.2d 870 (10th Cir. 1973).

32. Iowa Citizens, *infra* note 29, at 854.

33. Environmental Defense Fund, Inc. v. Corps of Engineers, 348 F. Supp. 916 (N.D. Miss. 1972).

34. Gillham I, *supra* note 17, at 759; Environmental Defense Fund, Inc. v. Corp of Engineers, 325 F. Supp., 749, 759 (E.D. Ark. 1971).

35. Donovan, *The Federal Government and Environmental Control: Administrative Reform on the Executive Level*, 12 BOST. COLL. INC. & COM. L. REV. 541, 553 (1972).

36. Natural Resources Defense Council, Inc. v. Morton, 458 F.2d 827, 834 (D.C. Cir. 1972).

37. Conservation Council of North Carolina v. Froehlke, 340 F. Supp. 222, 226 (M.D.N.C. 1972).

38. Sierra Club v. Froehlke, 486 F.2d 946 (7th Cir. 1973).

39. McPhail v. Corps of Engineers, __ F. Supp. __, __ 4 E.R.C. 1908, 1911 (E.D. Mich. 1972).

40. Environmental Defense Fund, Inc. v. Corps of Engineers, 470 F.2d 289, 297-300 (8th Cir. 1972).

41. *See, e.g.,* Pennsylvania Environmental Council v. Bartlett, 315 F. Supp. 238 (M.D. Pa. 1970), *aff'd*, 454 F.2d 613 (3d Cir. 1971); Brooks v. Volpe, 319 F. Supp. 90 (W.D. Wash. 1970) and 329 F. Supp. 118 (W.D. Wash. 1971); Investment Syndicates, Inc. v. Richmond, 318 F. Supp. 1038 (D. Ore. 1970).

42. Calvert Cliffs, *supra* note 27 at 1123.

43. Arlington Coalition, *supra* note 11, at 1332.

44. 372 F. Supp. 147 (N.D. Ill. 1973).

45. ___ F. Supp. ___ 6 E.R.C. 1064 (S.D. Cal. 1973).

46. *Supra* note 38.

47. 481 F.2d 1079 (D.C. Cir. 1973).

48. *Id*. at 1082.

INTRODUCTION

As environmental impact assessment has increasingly become an integral component of planning, assessment methodologies have grown in stature.[1] Briefly, a method of environmental assessment is defined as a means to arrange, present, and evaluate the natural, economic, aesthetic, social, and cultural effects, both direct and indirect, of a proposed project. Currently, more than twenty methods of measuring environmental impacts have been identified.[2] The object of this section is to briefly review the most promising of the more quantitative approaches to EIS with respect to small scale projects. No attempt has been made to review studies which focus on specialized projects such as manufacturing establishments, transportation systems, airports, oilports, or power plants.[3] As will be pointed out in the remainder of this section, each of the more advanced approaches to EIS has its own particular advantages and shortcomings of which the unwary EIS investigator must be made aware. As both the sophistication and cost of a technique increases, its applicability frequently decreases.

In 1973, the Illinois Institute for Environmental Quality produced a handbook for environmental impact statements which remains an excellent compendium for potential users.[4] Within this text, the Illinois group specifies a hierarchy of EIS methodologies. From the very general and nonquantitative to the very specific and quantitative, the hierarchy is specified as (a) multidisciplinary teams, (b) checklists, and (c) assessment tables and matrices. A category that is neglected in the text is the various modeling approaches.

The first category of EIS analysis is a largely individual approach to a specific area of environmental impact, in which aspects of the environment are investigated by an assemblage of experts. The analysis from an overall standpoint is frequently uneven, lumping in a single report nominal, ordinal, and interval data. Some impacts are treated in hundreds of pages, others in less than a page.

The second category of analysis, the checklist approach, is the level of analysis contained in this handbook. There is an effort to oversee the assessment: to recommend methods of investigation and to standardize inputs to provide predictable topic coverage and a relatively high level of replicability. Obviously, this method also has its shortcomings. It is more descriptive than comparative, and judgments about the positive or negative environmental impact of the project are not put before the reviewer in the form of a baseball score: 5 to 1, 4 to 4, etc.

The third category of analysis, assessment tables and matrices, will be demonstrated in this section of the handbook. This is a frequent extension of the checklist approach wherein each proposed *action* is identified as a *column* of a matrix, and the impacts are identified by reference to *rows* of the matrix. The Leopold method[5] of matrix analysis will be discussed and employed in an example. The McHargian land suitability mapping will also be discussed[6] although no examples will be employed. The latter approach is not the typical EIS matrix, but rather is a means to demonstrate *differences* in impacts and costs as a function of variation in land characteristics.

Category four, impact assessment via modeling, will only be breifly addressed. This method of analysis is extremely costly and therefore applicable only to the location of major facilities such as manufacturing plants, highways, and mines.

STRUCTURED INFORMATION: THE QUANTITATIVE IDEAL

In order to respond to the five general categories of information requested by various EIS formats, the analysis should have the following attributes:

1. As much quantification of decision-making information as possible;
2. A clear delineation of the spatial and temporal scope of the impacts with special attention focused on the choice of boundaries and on the definition of the area or areas of greatest impact;
3. A set of parameters which characterize the impacts and indicate their importance, both at the time of construction and during the operation of the proposed facility;
4. At least a minimal means of comparing the impacts so that important trade-offs and substitutions may be isolated; and
5. A means of identifying and measuring further projects likely to be induced by the proposed project.

Quantification of all information is difficult because data are frequently not available or are of dubious quality. However, it is precisely because the key element in the siting of activities is economic, and economic benefits are typically indicated even if not supported by strong underlying data, that quantification of environmental benefits and costs is needed. The user should classify data and information inputs on a scale which distinguishes excellent from poor data and hard, continuous data from subjective opinions. In short, the user should report in a quantitative format that will enhance credibility by indicating both the sources and reliability of information.

SEVERAL ASSESSMENT TABLE/MATRIX APPROACHES

Most of the impact statements mentioned earlier in the handbook have a few of the five attributes listed above. The vast majority of impact statements may be categorized as narrow, largely verbal commentaries without a comprehensive approach or a strong environmental focus. Undoubtedly the better impact statements have used prepared guidelines, although their availability is limited. The most familiar of the "beyond the checklist" studies was prepared by Leopold and associates and by self-admission is little more than a "sincere but still preliminary effort to fill an interim need."[7] The 13-page document provides a format of presentation, a scale for a numerical weighting system, and an 88 x 100 matrix of existing conditions and of actions which could cause impacts. Thus, we liken the information matrix to a gourmet chef's list of recipes. Unfortunately, the details of the recipes and the costs of the ingredients are not supplied.

The potential impacts of a proposed housing development, bridge, or road may be vaguely gleaned from the one to six word categories along the rows and columns of the matrix. The matrix may serve as a checklist; but in this role the user must be prepared to search for indirect effects among the categories. For example, a single row and column intersection is present for urbanization and water quality. However, about 30 other causative actions listed in the matrix may be associated with urbanization, and these proposed actions may, in turn, affect about 60 of the 88 existing characteristics of the present environment. In addition, the categories are too general (as seen in the one water quality category). Finally, the numerical weighting scheme (a scale of 1-10) is difficult to use for comparisons between parameters and, in turn, to obtain a total impact score.

The Leopold report is somewhat more advanced than other publications dealing with general categories of impacts—but the user will find that they can provide only some of the larger bones in a complex body of literature that spans the physical and social sciences.

McHarg's land use suitability mapping method provides a simple means of obtaining quantified, comparative, and aggregative measures of impact.[8] Briefly, parameters assumed to affect land use are mapped on transparencies on a scale of 1 to 5. All the parameters are of equal value and may be summed to obtain an aggregate suitability score by geographic area. Krauskopf and Bunde have built on McHarg's work by computerizing the mapping procedure and providing for the unequal weighting of parameters.[9] At present, variations of the land suitability techniques are gaining wide acceptance among local governments, although the implementing land use regulations lag to a considerable degree.

The two most complete and relatively inexpensive quantitative methods available today are more sophisticated versions and combinations of the weighted checklist and land suitability methods. One was developed by the Institute of Ecology of the University of Georgia for highway siting and the other by Battelle-Columbus for water resource projects.[10] Both try to include a large number of parameters (56 and 64, respectively) which characterize impacts likely to result from transportation and water resource activities. Both studies produce results which are comparative, weighted according to importance, and divisible into long and short term impacts.

The Battelle version is preferred by the authors for two reasons. First, it was funded by EPA and therefore should enjoy wide circulation and gain greater acceptance. Second, in comparison to the Georgia study, the Battelle methodology is adaptable to a wider range of environmental studies and, although more elaborate, is easier to use. Nonetheless the Battelle model has a number of shortcomings, several of which will be briefly reviewed at this point, and at the end of the section. In their attempts to be comprehensive and systematic, the Battelle staff had to prejudge the importance of incremental changes in the environment. These value judgments, which are biased toward water resource impacts, pervade the methodology. The user, therefore, should pay special attention to securing the best possible data, to indicating the adequacy of the data, and to reviewing the weights and ranges designed by Battelle in the local context.

In the hands of a group that will conscientiously seek to supply the information requested by NEPA or its progeny, the Battelle approach will serve as a useful guide to those who desire more than the checklist approach in impact analyses. In the hands of persons seeking short-cuts, this broad approach will yield results which, while quantitative and reasonably comprehensive for small projects, will be as unpalatable to the EIS purist as the many verbal or unweighted impact statements.

Beyond the Battelle study and the other naive models described above is the possibility of an impact analysis which makes use of more data, more sophisticated environmental modeling techniques, and more money. Three studies which illustrate different additions to the Battelle study were prepared by Ortolano, by Isard, and by Battelle.[11]

In the Ortolano study, twenty-five engineers, chemists, biologists, architects, lawyers, and geologists in a year-long interdisciplinary seminar sought means of measuring and of displaying environmental impacts. The seminar members concluded that "the complexity of the assessment task, and the diversity of situations in which it must be accomplished, preclude 'cookbook' or detailed programmed type methodology."[12] Instead they offer a conceptual framework for preparing impact analyses of physical, biological, and chemical impacts of impoundments, channelization, dredging, and spoil disposal.

Their procedure which is later modified in an illustrative study demonstrates the type of efforts that should be made in projects which are likely to be extremely costly or controversial. The sequence developed by the Ortolano group has five steps:[13]

1. Identify the important impacts and spatial and temporal boundaries with the aid of the checklist methodologies and local experts;
2. Develop initial forecasts on the basis of rule-of-thumb methods and easily available information;
3. Use these forecasts to identify priorities for major data gathering and analysis efforts;
4. Develop necessary data banks and prepare final impact forecasts; and
5. Integrate final forecasts.

Theoretically, an additional step should exist beyond the workable procedure advocated by the Ortolano group. One should be able to secure economic, social, and environmental data, develop interrelationships among these parameters as technological coefficients or equations, and translate the system of coefficients and equations into an optimizing model. Isard has developed an input-output model which incorporates a portion of this hypothetical approach. Battelle has prepared an environmental and economic trade-off model for Arizona which moves still closer to providing such a systematic and comprehensive mathematical decision-making model. And the authors and associates are working on a similar model for solid waste management in a region of four million people. These stately frameworks are likely to be cast aside at the local level, however, because a great deal of funds will be required to determine the direct and indirect relationships among the system parameters.

AN EXPLANATION OF THE ASSESSMENT
TABLE/MATRIX APPROACH

In the words of the Battelle staff, their Environmental Evaluations System (EES) "was designed to be comprehensive, systematic, interdisciplinary, and pragmatic."[14] In our opinion, the EES may be used for quick and rough estimates rather than a detailed examination of environmental impact. More refined analyses of parameters considered in a crude manner in the EES and an analysis of parameters and interrelationships not considered by the Battelle model may be warranted in many project evaluations. The EES will be reviewed in three steps: (1) output from the model; (2) input to the model; and (3) preparing an environmental assessment with a hypothetical illustration. This order is in recognition of the fact that most handbook users will be interested in the extent to which the methodology satisfies NEPA requirements. Fewer users will be interested in the information used in the analysis; still fewer will be interested in the processing of the information.

Output from the System

The EES provides a means of satisfying the requirements of NEPA.

Results include total impact scores ("environmental impact units") with and without the proposed project and with and without alternative projects, as well as the isolation of major adverse impacts ("red flags"). All results are in a quantitative form, amenable to validation by other groups and to a variety of sensitivity tests of the relative importance of particular parameters.

Input to the System

Since the results from quantitative modeling analyses are only as good as the input data, it is important to consider in some depth the information used in the environmental assessment model. The Battelle EES includes four major categories of information: ecological, physical/chemical, aesthetic, and social. The four categories include nineteen components, and the nineteen components include sixty-four parameters. Each of the components is assigned an importance index which is a proportion of 100. Exhibit C-1, which is reproduced from the Battelle report, indicates the categories, components, parameters, and weights ("impact units") that comprise the model.

Given the fact that the model was developed for water resource projects, it is not surprising that biochemical water quality and land use are assigned the highest impact unit values, while noise pollution and the aesthetic value of environmental composition are assigned the lowest weights. Users who are not proposing or evaluating projects which will have predominant effects on water resources will have to modify or develop new categories, components, and parameters and adjust the impact weights assigned to the components.

The heart, and one of the most controversial parts, of the Battelle approach is their method of scaling the parameters so that they are commensurate. To the scientist, planner, and engineer who has been modeling the impact of different discharges on the environment, the Battelle scaling method may be viewed as a travesty of science; conversely, to the public official and citizen, the sacrifice of some detail about the physical environment may be necessary in order to include aesthetic and social considerations in benefit/cost economic arguments.

The Battelle scaling approach should be considered in the context of alternative approaches. The simplest and cheapest approach is to describe the impacts. Quite obviously, there are the associated shortcomings. Verbal remarks may be erudite and incisive; however, more typically they are not incisive, not systematic, and not comprehensive. A second approach is to rate the impacts along a scale such as critical, average, or not important. A simple rating scheme is better than a purely verbal description, but falls short of providing commensurable results. At the other extreme, mathematical water quality models may be used to simulate the impact of a discharge of an oxygen-demanding waste on water quality with a high degree of accuracy.

The Battelle scaling procedure falls almost midway between our descriptive approach and the mathematical modeling approaches. A 0 to 1 index is developed for each parameter, where 1 indicates the best environmental quality and 0 indicates the worst environmental quality.

EXHIBIT C-1
Battelle Environmental Evaluation System
for Water Quality Management

I. 24 ECOLOGY
6 Terrestrial Species and Populations
Vegetation
Browsers and Grazers
Small Game Animals
Pests
6 Aquatic Species and Populations
Vegetation
Fish
Waterfowl
Pests
6 Terrestrial Habitats and Communities
Rare and Endangered Species
Species Diversity
6 Aquatic Habitats and Communities
Rare and Endangered Species
Special Diversity

II. 34 PHYSICAL/CHEMICAL
8 Biochemical Water Quality
Dissolved Oxygen
Inorganic Phosphate
Inorganic Nitrogen
Fecal Coliform
6 Chemical Water Quality
Hazardous Materials
Total Dissolved Solids
pH
6 Physical Water Environment
Basin Hydrologic Loss
Frequency of Extreme Flows
Temperature
Turbidity
4 Air Quality
Particulate Matter
Reactive Hydrocarbons
Sulfur Oxides
Nitrogen Oxides
8 Land Use
Location of Interceptors
Reserve
and Treatment Facilities
Soil Erosion
Solid Waste Disposal Controls
2 Noise Pollution
Frequency of Disturbing Noise
Intensity of Disturbing Noise

III. 24 AESTHETICS
4 Land
Surface Configuration
Land Appearance
Alignment of Stream, Reservoir and Estuary Shoreline
Geological Surface Material
3 Air
Odor
Visual
Sound
6 Water
Flow
Clarity
Water Level
Floating Material
5 Biota
Wooded Shoreline
Terrestrial Aniamls
Aquatic Life
Vegetation
4 Man-Made Structures
Architectural Design Structures
Compatibility with Other Structures and Natural Environment
Planting and Site Design
2 Composition
Composite Effect
Unique Composition

IV. 18 SOCIAL
5 Environmental Interests
Recreational Accessibility
Recreation Activities
Educational/Scientific
Historical/Cultural
6 Health and Safety
Accident Prevention
Buffer Zone Development
Facilities Location
System Overload
7 Community Well-Being
Community Involvement
Population Served by Sewers
Community Treatment Participation

Source: Norbert Dee, *et al., Planning Methodology for Water Quality Management Environmental Evaluation System*, Columbus, Ohio, Battelle-Columbus, July 1973, figure 8, p. 50.

These indices sacrifice information about the ecological and physical/chemical parameters and impose a dubious quantitative structure on aesthetic and social components.

The compromises made in constructing the indices may be illustrated by reviewing two of the more controversial indices: physical/chemical—dissolved oxygen; and biota—wooded shoreline. Dissolved oxygen (DO) is the most commonly used indicator of water quality. Typically, the higher the DO, the smaller the discharge of organic and other wastes into the water body and the better the water for recreation and for the maintenance of a heterogenous aquatic population. Low DO values hamper the reproduction, feeding, and ultimately the respiration capabilities of fish and aquatic organisms. Rivers with low dissolved oxygen have a limited number and variety of pollution-tolerant species (such as eel or pike) and are normally classified as unfit for contact recreation. If dissolved oxygen is absent from a water body, anaerobic decay will produce an unpleasant odor.

DO is measured in milligrams of oxygen per liter of water (mg/l) or parts per million (ppm). The critical range for DO is 2-6 ppm. Battelle casts the DO continuum from 0 to 14.6 ppm into four ranges (exhibit C-2). The authors would argue that the break should have been made at 3 and 6 ppm instead of 2 and 5 ppm because at DO levels below 3 ppm many species are seriously hindered.

EXHIBIT C-2
BATTELLE DISSOLVED OXYGEN INDEX

Range	Parameter Measurement (ppm)	Parameter Quality Index
1	$0 \leqslant DO \leqslant 2$	0.0
2	$2 < DO \leqslant 5$	0.2
3	$5 < DO \leqslant 7$	0.7
4	$7 < DO$	1.0

Source: Dee, *et al.*, *Planning Methodology*, p. 76.

DO levels above 7 and 8 ppm act as a buffer against shock effluent loads. The important conclusion to be drawn from this brief consideration of DO is that Battelle's grouping of DO into four ranges involves a loss of information about the impact of small changes in DO on the river ecosystem.

The biota—wooded shoreline parameter implies the converse problem of imposing a quantitative structure on aesthetic preferences. The wooded shoreline parameter is based on the assumption that a shoreline bordered by trees and shrubs is more pleasing than one which is not. The four ranges and associated parameter quality values are listed in exhibit C-3. In this case one can dispute the parameter quality index and the overriding assumption that a clearly defined shoreline is more pleasing.

EXHIBIT C-3
BATTELLE WOODED SHORELINE INDEX

Range	*Parameter Measurement*	*Parameter Quality Index*
1	no trees	0.0
2	some trees	0.5
3	half trees	0.8
4	predominantly trees	1.0

Source: Dee, *et al.*, *Planning Methodology*, p. 113.

Most of the other sixty-two parameters fall between DO and wooded shoreline with respect to the noise generated and information lost by casting them into ranges. Overall, while one can dispute the method of structuring the parameters, one cannot dispute the fact that the standardization of all the parameters makes the model easy to understand and to validate.

A second part of the Battelle model which should be reviewed in detail is the "environmental assessment tree." When quantitative values have been assigned, total environmental impact has normally been measured by accumulating the scores of all the parameters. The Battelle method interposes a step between the sixty-four parameters and the total impact score. Specifically, the scores of the parameters are aggregated into nineteen components with nineteen network trees which have been constructed to translate the relationship between the good and the bad values on individual parameters into good and bad values for a set of parameters.

Exhibit C-4 is a reproduction of part of the Aquatic Species and Populations Assessment Tree. To obtain the environmental assessment one first determines the range of the vegetation parameter, and then follows the arrow to the next parameter box (waterfowl). The same dichotomy is offered at the next parameter (pests), depending upon the answer to the initial parameter. After following several more branches on the tree, a last branch will intersect the environmental quality scale and provide a score for the component. For example, parameter ratings of 3 in vegetation, 4 in waterfowl, 3 in pests, and 3 in fish may be followed by the dashed lines to an assessment of 0.85 along the tree. The final rating after two more steps on the tree is 0.79 which signals an environment of good quality.

The advantages of the assessment tree are that it is simple to use, requires less precise data about individual parameters, and places the single parameter in the context of the real-world interrelationships among similar variables. The disadvantage of the assessment tree approach is the further loss of information about individual parameters.

Four other characteristics of the Battelle model deserve a brief review: First, major impacts ("red flags") are defined by a change of two ranges. For example, in the DO case (exhibit C-2), if a proposed outfall could reduce DO from range 4 ($7 < DO$) to range 2 ($2 < DO \leqslant 5$), the project should be seriously

EXHIBIT C-4
BATTELLE AQUATIC SPECIES AND POPULATION ASSESSMENTS TREE

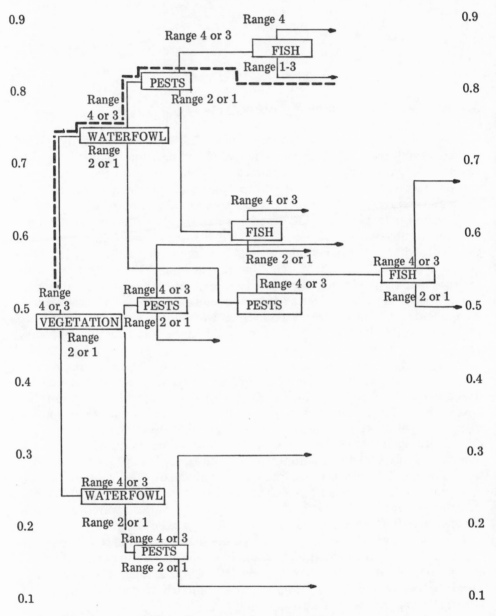

Source: Dee, *et. al.*, Planning Methodology, figure A-2.

considered for rejection. Second, the user weighs the impacts with respect to their long and short term importance. Third, the research team that prepared the model was interdisciplinary—a practice that should be continued by those preparing impact analyses. Finally, public participation is strongly advocated and indeed is built into the model at several stages.

The use of ranges for parameters, assessment trees to group the parameters, and "red flags" to define critical impacts clearly simplifies the job of the analyst, allows the work to be evaluated by persons who are not specialists, and tends to assure consideration of some impacts which otherwise might have been neglected due to a reluctance to mix qualitative and quantitative information. The major limitations of the Battelle system include the facts that it was designed only for water resources studies, forces all forms of information into a similar form, and evaluates impact components independently of their potential induced effect upon other components.

AN EXAMPLE OF THE ASSESSMENT
TABLE/MATRIX APPROACH

We have generalized the Battelle approach, principally through rewording, into a sequence which can serve as a reasonable guideline irrespective of whether the reader wishes to use the Battelle EES. The sequence (exhibit C-5) will be illustrated with a proposed publicly assisted housing project for 500 families in a town with a population of 25,000. The hypothetical town has an area of 16 square miles and lies in the outer suburbs of a small metropolitan region. Exhibit C-6 is a sketch of the town showing the location of the two potential housing sites and an inset of the town's regional setting.

Initial Qualitative Assessment of the Environment
Without the Project

The initial step is to determine the present status of the environment in the town. Major problems identifed by the town planners and by the public might include the following:

   a. An insufficient number of garden apartment units for young families, unmarried persons, and older individuals and families;
   b. The rapidly rising cost of providing public services; and
   c. A fear of losing recreation and undeveloped lands to developers.

Assess the Environment Without the Proposed Project

At this stage the parameters and the component assessment trees (if the Battelle model is used) are used to establish base numbers for the environment without the proposed housing project. The Battelle approach

EXHIBIT C-5

STEPS IN PREPARING AN IMPACT ASSESSMENT

Study the Proposed Project
↓
Initial Qualitative Assessment of the Environment
Without the Proposed Project
↓
Quantitative Assessment of the Environment
Without the Proposed Project
↓
Delineate Goals and Set Priorities
↓
Assess the Environmental Impact
of the Proposed Project
↓
Assess the Environmental Impact of Alternatives
↓
Comment on the Five NEPA Questions
↓
Make Recommendations

can be used to develop rough numbers for all relevant parameters and to isolate critical environmental impacts. Special attention should be paid to areas likely to be directly affected by the two sites, to environmentally sensitive attributes of the environment, and to areas likely to receive major induced impacts from the proposed project (as in the case of sites for roads or shopping centers). The extent to which an analysis should go beyond the Battelle approach depends solely upon the complexity of local conditions. We must emphasize that the Battelle and checklist approaches should not be used so exclusively as to excuse the analyst from identifying an important environmental benefit or from missing a serious environmental cost.

Delineate Goals and Set Priorities

Given the status quo analysis as background data, a project analysis may follow two paths. If the project has been proposed by a developer, then a specific project-site combination must be judged in the context of the problems cited above and in the context of alternative sites picked by the responsible agency. If the town is planning the project, then alternative sites should be chosen to come as close as possible to balancing priorities set by officials and by the public. We have assumed that the sample project was proposed by a developer at site 1, and that the following ranked priorities were developed for the town after public meetings:

a. Provide 500 garden apartment units;
b. Control the direction of development in the town; and
c. Avoid development in the best forest areas, in the floodplain, and in other environmentally sensitive areas.

Assess the Environmental Impact of the Proposed Project

Next, the status of the expected environment during construction and throughout the life of the proposed project should be estimated using the same methods as in the assessment of no project construction. The difference between the assessment with and without the proposed project is the impact. The major negative impacts if the project was constructed at site 1 might include the following:

a. Loss of forest land and disruption of the environment in the forest;
b. Need to treat the sewage from the housing project either in a package plant or by building an interceptor. Many states will not permit the construction of package plants and EPA will not fund interim projects. If an interceptor is constructed, the town may be able to use it as a guide to control growth. Normally, however, towns are unable to prevent an interceptor from acting as a magnet for land uses that they consider undesirable;
c. A serious runoff problem during construction and a continuing,

EXHIBIT C-6
MAP OF HYPOTHETICAL STUDY AREA

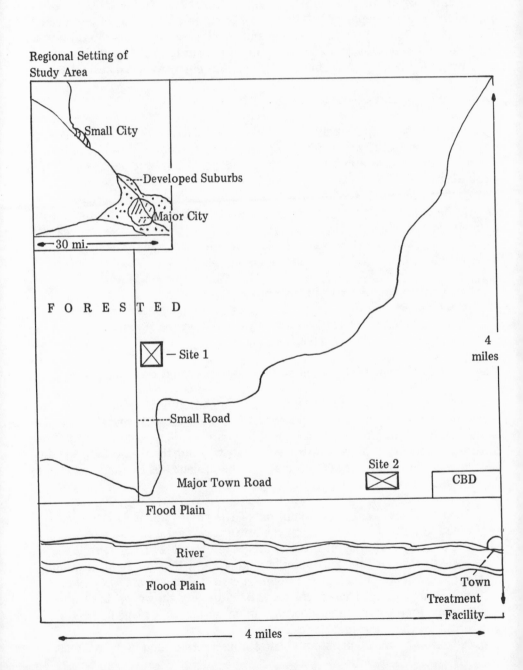

Regional Setting of
Study Area

Small City

----Developed Suburbs

Major City

←— 30 mi.—→

F O R E S T E D

⊠ — Site 1

----------Small Road

Site 2

Major Town Road　　　　⊠　　　　CBD

Flood Plain

River

Flood Plain

4
miles

Town
Treatment
Facility

←———— 4 miles ————→

though smaller problem thereafter due to the clearing of land for the housing project, and for associated commercial and institutional developments, for roads, and for the interceptor; and

d. Serious noise and air pollution problems during construction and solid wastes which must be cleared.

Assess the Environmental Impact of the Alternative

The major negative impacts of the site 2 alternative might include the following:

a. Loss of land potentially valuable for industrial, institutional, and commercial development to housing;
b. More and slower moving traffic along the major thoroughfare and in the CBD;
c. Serious noise and air pollution problems during construction and solid wastes which must be cleared.

Comment on the Five NEPA or NEPA Progeny Questions

a. The major direct environmental impacts of the proposed project at site 1 include a loss of forest lands, decimation of terrestrial and aquatic species and the populations that depend upon them. These impacts should be displayed in quantitative forms along with all the other negative and positive impacts of the project.
b. Adverse impacts that cannot be avoided are serious in the case of site 1 because of a loss of a portion of the forest land and the disruption of the ecosystem in adjoining sections,the possibility of uncontrolled growth resulting from the interceptor, and an increase in runoff. Both sites 1 and 2 will suffer from noise and air pollution impacts during construction.
c. The relationship between local short term uses of man's environment and the maintenance and enhancement of a long term productivity at site 1 are, in essence, focused around the relatively short term use of the land for a housing complex and the long term costs to the forest ecosystem.
d. If the housing project is constructed at site 1, the major irreversible and irretrievable commitments of resources would include a portion of the forest, an interceptor and collection system, and an expanded road system to serve the site.
e. Overall, site 2 is strongly recommended over site 1 for the proposed project.

NOTES

1. R. C. Viohl, Jr. and Kenneth G. M. Mason, *Environmental Impact Assessment Methodologies: An Annotated Bibliography*, Exchange Bibliography 691, Monticello, Ill., Council of Planning Librarians, November 1974, p. 4.

2. J. L. Moore, D. E. Manty, P. B. Cheney, J. L. Rhuman, *A Methodology for Evaluating Manufacturing Environmental Impact Statements for Delaware's Coastal Zone*, Columbus, Ohio, Battelle-Columbus, June 1973, p. 18.

3. See for example, J. Moore, *et al., ibid.*; A. G. Christianson, *Reviewing Environmental Impact Statements: Power Plant Cooling Systems, Engineering Aspects*, Corvallis, Oregon, Pacific Northwest Environmental Research Lab, October 1973; J. B. Burnham, M. H. Karr, G. L. Wilfert, W. S. Maynard, S. M. Nealey, I. Jones, *Technique for Environmental Decision Making Using Quantified Social and Aesthetic Values*, Seattle, Washington, Battelle Pacific Northwest Labs, February 1974; CLMI Systems, Inc., *Airports and Their Environment*, prepared for U.S. Department of Transportation, Cambridge, Mass., September 1972; J. E. Finn and R. S. Reimers, *Development of Predictions of Future Pollution Problems*, Columbus, Ohio, Battelle-Columbus, March 1974; Chase, Rosen, and Wallace, Inc., *The State of the System (SOS) Model: Measuring Growth Limitations Using Ecological Concepts*, Alexandria, Va., February 1974; O. Saverlender, *The Highway Corridor: Predicting the Consequences of Alternative Highway Locations*, University Park, Pa., Pennsylvania Transportation and Traffic Safety Center, 1972; Federal Highway Administration, Socio-Economic Studies Division, Office of Program and Policy Planning, *Social and Economic Effects of Highways*, Washington, D.C., May 1974; and L. Thomas, D. Elcock, L. Gsellman, and S. Wilcox, *Socio-Economic Impact Analysis of the Proposed Sterling Power Plant*, McLean, Virginia, Mitre Corporation, August 1974.

4. D. Lewis, *Environmental Impact Statements: A Handbook for Writers and Reviewers*, Champaign, Ill., Illinois Institute for Environmental Quality, 1973; M. Warner's recent doctoral dissertation, *Environmental Impact Analysis: An Examination of Three Methodologies*, University of Wisconsin, Madison, 1973, also presents a comprehensive review of techniques.

5. L. Leopold, F. Clarke, B. Hanshaw, and T. Balsey, *A Procedure for Evaluating Environmental Impact*, Circular 645, 1971. Washington, D.C. U.S. Geological Survey, 1971.

6. I. McHarg, *Design with Nature*, Garden City, N.Y., The Natural History Press, 1969.

7. L. Leopold *et al., Procedure.*

8. I. McHarg, *Design.*

9. T. M. Krauskopf and D. C. Bunde, "Evaluation of Environmental Impact Through a Computer Modelling Process," in R. B. Ditton and T. L. Goodale, eds., *Environmental Impact Analysis: Philosophy and Methods*, Madison, Wisc., University of Wisconsin Sea Grant Publication, 1972, pp. 107-125.

10. Institute of Ecology, University of Georgia, *Optimum Pathway Matrix Analysis Approach to the Environmental Decision Making Process, Testcase: Relative Impact of Proposed Highway Alternative,* Athens, Ga., Institute of Ecology, 1971; and Norbert Dee, Neil Drobny, Janet Baker, Kenneth Duke, and David Fahringer, *Planning Methodology for Water Quality Management Environmental Evaluation System*, Columbus, Ohio, Battelle-Columbus, July 1973.

11. L. Ortolano, ed., *Analyzing the Environmental Impacts of Water Projects,* Alexandria, Virgina, U.S. Army Corps of Engineers, Institute for Water Resources, 1973; W. Isard, *Ecologic-Economic Analysis for Regional Development*, New York, Free Press, 1972; and Battelle-Columbus,

Development of the Arizona Environmental and Economic Trade Off Model, Columbus, Ohio, March, 1973.

12. L. Ortolano, *Impacts of Water Projects*, Foreword.

13. Ibid., ch. 4.

14. Dee, *et al., Planning Methodology*, p. ii.

ACKNOWLEDGMENTS

This study was accomplished at the urging of George Sternlieb, Director of the Rutgers University, Center for Urban Policy Research.

Two institutions very familiar to the housing field were immeasurably supportive of this project. Both the Urban Land Institute and the National Association of Home Builders turned over their entire EIS files to the research team. In this vein perhaps most useful of all were the letters written to both organizations by members asking for information or documents which would clarify the process they saw looming before them. The nature of these queries contributed greatly to the format and emphasis of the handbook. We would like to thank Messrs. Donald E. Priest, Randall W. Scott, and Dallas D. Miner of ULI and Mr. Rochell Brown, Jr. of NAHB for their sustained cooperation.

Procedures and requirements for EIS filings in the public sector under various U.S. Department of Housing and Urban Development guidelines were gleaned from HUD documents and from personal interviews with Mr. James Shuman, Ms. Donna Letwin and Mr. David Muddari of the Office of Environmental Planning (HUD). Their patience, especially that of Ms. Letwin and Mr. Muddari, is greatly appreciated.

Our colleagues at the Rutgers University College of Environmental Science, Department of Environmental Resources, were particularly helpful in suggesting changes and format emphases which would improve the monograph. Special credit must be given here to Drs. Leland G. Merrill, Jr., George Nieswand and James K. Mitchell, Professor B. Budd Chavooshian, and Thomas P. Norman, Esq. for their willingness not only to donate their materials but to comment on the document in a very brief period of time.

Jerome G. Rose, Esq., Professor of Urban Planning and Policy Development is an always willing critic of extremely high calibre. His comments aided our refining of both the progeny and legal history sections.

Mr. Harold Schwartz of the planning firm of Abeles & Schwartz, Inc., also offered his comments within a very tight time frame.

The clerical staff at the Center for Urban Policy Research is extremely proficient. Under the tutelage of Ms. Mary Picarella, office manager, and Mrs. Joan Frantz, head typist, Ms. Connie Michaelson, Ms. Lydia Lombardi and Ms. Elizabeth Batchelder ground out the manuscript in steadfast fashion.

Ms. Carol Rosen edited and shaped the manuscript and Ms. Linda Hutchison is responsible for its distribution.

Finally, our joint authors were superb. Their substantive knowledge of EIS content and procedure enabled the document to reach fruition. We hope we have represented their efforts both clearly and honestly and within the context of their original submissions.